THE BEAR

WHO STOLE THE

CHINOOK

TALES FROM THE BLACKFOOT

FRANCES FRASER

INTRODUCTION BY HUGH A. DEMPSEY

Douglas & McIntyre
Vancouver/Toronto

For the memory of Steven Williams, my father, who knew and loved the Siksika; and for D. Alexander Fraser, who was also interested in them.

For my mother, Viola Giberson Williams, who tried to give me "every good thing," with my love and gratitude.

Copyright © 1959, 1968 by Frances Fraser

First Douglas & McIntyre edition 1990
90 91 92 93 94   5 4 3 2 1

Originally published by Macmillan of Canada as *The Bear Who Stole the Chinook and Other Stories* and *The Wind along the River*.

Douglas & McIntyre
1615 Venables Street
Vancouver, British Columbia V5L 2H1

Canadian Cataloguing in Publication Data

Fraser, Frances, 1920–1989.
   The bear who stole the Chinook

   Previously published separately as: The bear who stole the Chinook and other stories and The wind along the river.

   ISBN 0-88894-685-6

   1. Siksika Indians - Legends. 2. Indians of North America - Alberta - Legends. I. Title.
E99.S54F72 1990   398.2'08997   C90-091097-6

Design by Alexandra Hass
Typeset by The Typeworks
Printed and bound in Canada by D. W. Friesen & Sons Ltd.
Printed on acid-free paper ∞

Contents

Introduction

Throughout her life, Frances Fraser had close connections with the Blackfoot people of southern Alberta. Her paternal grandfather, John Williams, had been farming in the Queenstown-Milo area of Alberta, just south of the Blackfoot Reserve, since 1905. He worked closely with the native people and was given the name of Kisistoyi, or Pointed Beard. The farm where Frances was raised was also close to the reserve; her father, Steve Williams, was the reserve's government farm inspector for a time, and he was known to the Blackfoot as Natosistahkapi, or Sun Coming Down.

As Fran was growing up, there were many Blackfoot visitors to the family farm. Sometimes the Indians came to sell fence posts or to help with the harvesting; at other times they just dropped in for a cup of tea. Little Frances was curious about these men with names like Ben Calf Robe, Crooked Meat Strings and The Sleigh, with their hair in braids and their feet clad in moccasins or cowboy boots. She soon understood many of their words and picked up a working knowledge of the Blackfoot language. During this time she too was given a name: Sokosinik-sinaki, or Good Singing Woman.

One day, Fran's father received a visit from Many Shots, one of the patriarchs of the tribe. Many Shots proudly displayed the scars he had sustained by undergoing the self-torture ritual of his tribe. As a young man, he had vowed to perform the ritual to fulfill a promise to the sun spirit. At the next Sun Dance, he had permitted the holy men to drive skewers into his chest; these were attached to ropes fastened to the Sun Dance centre pole, and while the rest of the tribe looked on, he danced and tugged against the ropes until the skewers were ripped from his breast.

Frances noticed that a couple of Many Shots's fingers had been amputated at the first joints. These, she discovered, had been cut off as a sign of mourning upon the death of one of the old man's close relatives.

The little girl's worry about this strange man turned to fear when Many Shots picked her up, sat her on his knee and began singing Blackfoot songs to her. It was an experience she would never forget, and from then on, she never seemed to be very far away from the Blackfoot.

Frances Fraser was born Frances Jane Williams on October 12, 1920 in Bassano, Alberta. Raised by her parents Steven and Viola Williams on their farm and educated in the local towns of Queenstown and Cluny, Fran continued to think of herself as a farm girl for the rest of her life. Even though her mother was the local correspondent for the *Calgary Herald*, the young Frances showed no interest in becoming a writer. Her father recruited her to write short narratives to accompany the pictures in a scrapbook he was compiling on the Blackfoot, but that was the closest she got to any kind of literary enterprise in her early years.

In 1936, Fran's regular routines on her parents' farm in Cluny were disrupted when she suffered an accident. With her leg in a cast, she was unable to do the cooking, cleaning and other chores that usually occupied her time. During her convalescence, she was visited by old friends from the Blackfoot Reserve, who passed the hours by telling her stories. As Frances later told Ken Liddell, a columnist for the *Calgary Herald,* some of her visitors asked if she would write these stories down for posterity "because their children wouldn't listen, and the time was approaching when the stories would be lost forever."

Frances married Frank Fraser in 1942, and shortly afterwards they moved to Frank's family farm near High River, Alberta. Here Fran launched into her chosen career as the distaff side of a small farming operation. She continued to work on her Blackfoot stories, but most of her time was taken up by the normal activities of a farm homemaker: raising three children (Margery, Alex and Gordon), working in the home, driving the tractor, helping to brand the cattle and performing other chores on the 1500-acre farm.

The Frasers developed a large pond on their land into a recreation site, stocking it with rainbow trout and allowing its use by canoeists. Friends often came on weekends just to camp. Fran was active with the order of the Eastern Star, serving as Worthy Matron of the local chapter; she also belonged to the United Farm Women of Alberta and was an avid supporter of the local Museum of the Highwood.

Fran's initial writing efforts appeared in the *High River Times* and soon the rural editor for the *Calgary Herald* invited her to submit her stories. Her first article for the *Herald* appeared on May 2, 1956. By summer, she had a regular column entitled "Off the Reservation," which featured old Blackfoot legends and children's stories as well as discussions of more current matters. One early piece described buffalo jump sites in the High River area, while another paid tribute to the efforts of Joe Little Chief in trying to preserve the legends of his tribe.

Prior to this time, few people had written about the Plains Indians with any regularity. Readers became curious about the byline "Fran Fraser," wondering whether it might be a nom de plume for some well-known Calgary author. The *Herald* received so many inquiries that the rural editor devoted his entire July 11, 1958 column to the paper's new discovery.

"'Who is this Fran Fraser? What's her real name?'" he began. "Apart from being able to say that Fran Fraser was the writer's real name, that she had been closely associated with the Blackfoot Indians since infancy, there was little more light that I could shed on the matter. Mrs. Fraser is a farm wife—the homestead is seven miles southeast of High River—and she's kept mighty busy raising three children. . . . The column she writes periodically for the *Herald* could be described as a service to the Indians as much as being of interest to the white man. Financial returns from this undertaking are not great, but Mrs. Fraser takes great pride in the fact that the Indians have enough confidence in her to tell her of the past."

With encouragement from W. O. Mitchell, who lived nearby, Frances began to sell some of her articles to the *Globe & Mail*'s weekly magazine, where they came to the attention of several book publishers. In 1959, Macmillan of Canada published her first book, *The Bear Who Stole the Chinook and Other Stories*. It was an instant success and was reprinted three times over the next dozen years. In 1960, Gage published two of her stories, "The People of the Many Chiefs" and "How Fire Came to the Prairies," as well as a poem, "Death of a Blackfoot Chief," in an anthology for children. So popular was her work that all three of her submissions were accepted, in spite of the fact that there were only forty-two pieces in the entire anthology and the publishers had received more than nine thousand entries. Her writing appeared in the next two Gage anthologies and, in 1968, Frances followed up her earlier success with a second book from Macmillan, *The Wind along the River*.

During these years Fran Fraser was accepted as an authority on the Blackfoot. She was a familiar figure at the Indian village during the Calgary Stampede; she helped the city's Heritage Park to research the painted tepees it had on display and assisted the Glenbow Museum in recording songs and ceremonies on the Blackfoot Reserve. She was also in demand as a public speaker and guest lecturer.

Her range of topics broadened during this time; she wrote about the history of the Queenstown-Milo area, early coal mining, the 1918 flu epidemic and other historical events. Because of some stories told to her by Milo pioneers, she launched a major study into the short life of the Ku Klux Klan in southern Alberta.

Yet in spite of her instant success as a writer, her active work in collecting stories, and the recognition she received, Fran never published another book. She had signed her contract with Macmillan excitedly and, she later believed, naively. She continued to write stories for the *Calgary Herald* and to carry out her research, but when Macmillan showed no interest in any more of her work, she entered a long and bitter period in her life. She believed that she was being stifled as an author and denied the opportunity to capitalize on her earlier successes. As her health declined over the following years, she had the feeling that success had passed her by. While Canadian writing became more and more popular and Canadian publishers more active, she saw herself as having been left in the backwash of the 1960s.

In 1988, Douglas & McIntyre decided to reissue her two earlier works in a single volume. However, Frances

Fraser's medical condition continued to deteriorate, and she died on April 20, 1989 at the age of sixty-eight, a year before this new edition of her work was published.

There can be no question that Frances Fraser understood the Blackfoot Indians and that they respected her. One of her most pleasurable moments came when a Blackfoot friend referred to *The Bear Who Stole the Chinook* as "our book." Fran would spend hours with elders, asking questions, writing their stories and nodding as they explained the customs and traditions of the tribe. If she was interviewing an old man, his wife would be nearby in the kitchen, keeping the cups filled with steaming hot tea as she listened to the familiar tales. The atmosphere was more relaxed when Fran visited a Blackfoot woman; the two would sit in the kitchen talking and often laughing at some ridiculous or ribald comment about the menfolk.

Central to Fran's collection of stories are those about Na-pe, the Old Man, the mythical trickster-creator of the Blackfoot tribe. He has no Christian counterpart, for Na-pe was never considered to be a good and all-powerful god. Rather, he had all the foibles and weaknesses of a human while possessing the supernatural power of a creator. He made the earth and the animals; he created the prairies, mountains and forests; and he made the first man and woman. He also made such momentous decisions as whether or not humans should have eternal life.

During his travels through Blackfoot country, Na-pe had many adventures, some of which revealed his stupidity, greed or callousness while others displayed his gifts for goodness and gratitude. The stories about the Old Man may be hilariously funny or tragically sad. Traditionally, they were told to boys and girls during cold winter nights. The stories served as lessons in life, showing the realities of the world and explaining the vagaries of nature. At the same time, they were a captivating form of entertainment for young and old. Frances collected many of these stories and chose the best (or most suitable) for her books. Some of the Na-pe stories, she explained to Ken Liddell, were "brutal and not exactly for children."

The rest of her stories fall into three categories: heroic adventures, general legends and religious tales. Some, like "The War-Trail of Sin'opa" and "The Man Who Couldn't Be Killed," are based on the adventures of real people in the nineteenth century. Others, such as "How the Thunder Made Horses" and "The Moon and the Seven Singers," are entirely mythological, while still others, like "The Girl Who Married the Morning Star" and "The Ghost Pipe," are important legends which explain how certain religious practices came to the tribe.

During her research, Frances found that some stories were almost family heirlooms and she felt greatly honoured when they were shared with her. She realized that, among a people who had no written language, the accuracy of story-telling was extremely important. An elder would recount a tale as it had been told to him or her, repeating conversations just as though he or she had witnessed the event personally. Frances wrote her stories to be read aloud, and she was pleased when the Blackfoot commended her for carrying on this tradition.

As Ken Liddell commented in his February 17, 1965 column, "The Blackfoot have offered many tributes to Mrs. Fraser for her work. One of the most heartening, from her point of view so far as accuracy was concerned, was when some of her stories were sung and danced and came out on the right beat and with the right foot forward. No mean trick, allowing for the translation."

In recording and writing these stories, Frances Fraser

has provided a valuable service. For the Blackfoot, she has preserved a fragile segment of their oral history, placing it in a permanent form where it can serve as an inspiration to young people for years to come. For non-Indians, she has shown what the native people believed, how they educated their children and how story-telling was an integral part of daily life, providing a tiny but important insight into one of Canada's original cultures.

Hugh A. Dempsey
Associate Director, Glenbow Museum

The Story-teller Speaks

The dark comes a little earlier to the Reservation these days. The sun goes down behind the sand hills, leaving the western sky arched with a clear and shining green. The air has peculiar clearness—the bells from the Mission can be heard for miles, and the long floating wails of train whistles come back from the cutbanks at the river.

This is Ke-to'ye ke-sum, the Moon of the Eater. Crackling frost underfoot warns the wayfarer that he had best not linger on the road; and up on the Cree Jump, A-pe'si the coyote wakes a weird echo with his salute to the Eater's Moon.

Over across the CPR tracks, now, the lights come on in the town, and the Indians lounging in stores and restaurants begin to disperse. Bright-blanketed women gather their parcels and their children. The guttural music of Blackfoot dialect is lost in the sudden beat of horse hoofs, the scrattle of iron-shod wheels on the gravel road. Car lights drift out past the Monument; and down toward South Camp, a coyote takes up the barking of dogs by the river, and makes of it a theme of lonely desolation.

During the day, the white man's world and the white man's ways hold sway over the Reservation; but with the coming of darkness, the wheat fields, the big tractors, the cross-surmounted spires of the Mission vanish, and the old gods come from their hiding.

This is the time when the white man on the Reservation walks a little faster, uneasily feeling that alien spirits are walking abroad in the night, eluding his knowledge, and contemptuous of his superiority.

Lamps begin to twinkle in the houses. Food is set out. People come together. Ke-to'ye ke-sum is a time for visiting, for singing the old songs, for telling and retelling the old tales. Now, the Old Ones come into their own, eagerly sought after as entertainers, for few present the tribal lore as they can. The sweet pungency of kínikínik fills the small frame houses, and the tea-kettle is seldom off the stove. The cups of sik'si-ki'me, the bitter, black boiled tea, laced with canned milk, and sugar, are passed from hand to hand, and thus refreshed, the story-tellers are ready.

So, we listen; and the quavering old voices rise high in their recreation of lost youth, and lost glory; and in that recounting of brave deeds, of trophies won, the coup-songs.

And the young men come, a bit more sceptical, more easily bored than their elders, but still attentive. They, who count a drab coup of cows milked, acres ploughed, listen wistfully, seeing themselves as they might have been; mourning, too, though perhaps they do not know it, abandoned pride, lost honour. Perhaps the Old Ones tell how the Eater's Moon came by its name; of the old days when only unremitting effort and ceaseless vigilance kept food in the tepees, and how, sometimes, when the Eater, the bitter cold of winter, brought heavy storms, and the buffalo had gone far away, hunger sat in the lodges of the Siksika.

Perhaps it is a tale of "old, unhappy, far-off things; of battles long ago," a story of old cruelty, long-remembered heartbreak. It may be the history of trophies—one of the Pipes, or the shield of Never-Sits-Down. There may be a love story: a warrior brings back

2

his beloved from the land of the dead; a maiden marries a star. The dramatic has a place too; the Snake becomes a brave of the tribe, a band of ghostly horses sweeps across the prairie, and the High Gods, interesting themselves in the affairs of men, share their medicine with the brave and the resourceful. And always, of course (when the company is right) there are the happy, rollicking tales of Na'pe, the eternal Old Man.

And there is laughter, and the soft cadence of our own language, the camaraderie of our own people. The satisfying fragrance of kínikínik, the pulse-beat of the dance drums—these are things for which an Indian has always a little hunger in his soul, no matter how long he is away from the Reservation, nor how far afield he may wander. This is home—no-ko-wa-ye—safe, and warm, and familiar.

And outside the house the Eater prowls; and outside the Reservation the world, to us, seems cold, and hostile, and alien. And because it is so, these old legends, these old songs, this colour of our heritage are the more treasured.

A Song for Lone Warrior

It was about this time of year—the Moon of the Eater—that the war chief, Lone Warrior, went out on a raid. He travelled by night, and he travelled alone, for this was his custom, and this was how he had gotten the name he bore—"Lone Warrior."

He was a man of many coups, this Lone Warrior. Many a scalp had hung from his lance, many a far-off enemy lodge had known his war-cry, and many a fine horse had carried him home. There was no lack of a tribesman who would have been happy to have accompanied him—so noted a chief—but Lone Warrior declined all companionship.

He went on foot, eastward, away from the setting sun. For many dark hours he travelled, until, upon the late moon's rising, he came to where a painted lodge stood alone on the prairie. He circled it, warily, but no dogs barked. There was no stir of picketed horses. When he came nearer, he saw the rawhide ropes binding it, the close-placed stones along the edge, and he knew this was a ghost lodge, a tepee in which the bodies of the dead had been placed, together with the provisions and gear needed for the souls' sojourn in the Sand Hills.

Then, from inside the tepee, he heard voices, the sound of a drum, and a song. Now Lone Warrior was a brave, or perhaps merely an unimaginative, man—they are often the same thing. So he walked boldly to the tepee entrance, and hailed those within. A voice answered, and bade him enter. He did so. Inside the lodge a fire burned (though no people were visible) and a pipe loaded with kínikínik, and lighted, lay beside it. The pipe was lifted suddenly and began a circuit of the tepee as if it were being passed from hand to hand. When it came to Lone Warrior, he took it and smoked it, then held it to his left side, and felt it taken from his hand. Four times the pipe went round, and when Lone Warrior had smoked for the fourth time, he looked about and saw that the tepee was filled with people. An old chief sat at the back, in the place of honour. He motioned Lone Warrior to a place at his side.

"Are you not afraid, here in this lodge of ghosts?" the old chief asked him.

Lone Warrior looked at him coldly. "I never feared a living man," he said. "I am not likely to be afraid of a dead one!"

"Where are your men?" asked the Ghost Chief. "Do you go raiding alone?"

"And I count my coups alone!" said Lone Warrior. He took the drum from the ghost-warrior who held it, and the high rolling chant of his coup-song (the recounting of all his triumphs and brave deeds) shook the lodge-poles.

When the song was finished the Ghost Chief ordered the women to make a feast for the guest. Then the drum went round the circle, and each ghostly warrior in turn related his adventures, the Ghost Chief last, as was proper. When the meal was ready, Lone Warrior ate with the spectres, and afterwards was entertained with dances and songs, and more tales of valour.

At last, the Ghost Chief said to him, "It is near dawn, brother, and you must leave us; but you are a brave man, and we wish to give you a gift—a medicine song, which you can use always. It is good luck to a raider! You may walk through the midst of an enemy camp without being seen, and come safe home without being wounded." And he took the drum and taught this song to Lone Warrior. Then Lone Warrior took the drum and sang the song himself, and when the final shout died away, he looked about him. The light of dawn was strengthening in the tepee now, and his companions of the night were gone. The fire was a circle of black stones, with cold ashes where flames had been, and throughout the lodge were only skeletons, in the place of the singers of a moment ago.

Lone Warrior rose, and laid the drum at the feet of the Ghost Chief—or rather, by the heap of bones where the Ghost Chief had been seated. "I will come again, to count coup with you," he promised, and went on his way. He returned to his own people with the spoils of a successful raid, and though he never returned to count another coup with the ghosts, from that time forward their song sent off raid-bound warriors. Lone Warrior lived to be a very old man, and died in his sleep, having never been wounded in battle.

The Bear Who Stole the Chinook

In this long-ago year, the snow came early, and lay deep, the wind blew from the north, cold and bitter, and the Chinook did not come. The Indians shivered in their lodges, for the snow made it hard to get wood for the fires. After a while, their food was gone. The children cried with hunger, and the hunters could find no game at all—everything had been driven away by the blizzards. Every morning, and every night, the Old Ones went out to look for the great, clear, blue arch that tells of the coming of the Chinook. But the grey clouds lay flat on the mountains and the Chinook did not come. In this camp there was a poor orphan boy, living alone. He suffered even more than the others did, for his tepee was old and tattered, and his clothing ragged. The others in the tribe did not think much of him, and his only friends were the birds and the animals. He talked to them, and often they shared his scanty food. Now, he called upon them for help.

A-pe'si, the coyote, came, and Se-pe'tso, the owl, and his family, Ma-mi'as-sik-ami, the magpie, and A-pau, the weasel. They sat down in the poor boy's lodge, to talk. If it would only get warmer, they said. The magpie, you know, is a dreadful gossip. He goes everywhere, and sees everything and, consequently, quite often he knows more than ordinary folk. So they asked him a question: What had become of the Chinook?

"For myself," said Ma-mi'as-sik-ami, "I do not know. But I have many relatives, and many of them live in the mountains. Some of them will know. I shall go ask them." And he flew away. After a while, he came back. "My relatives say," he told them, "that there is a great bear living far back in the mountains. He has stolen the Chinook, and he is keeping it fastened up in his lodge, so that he may be warm all winter."

The friends held a council of war. They decided that they would go to the mountains and set the Chinook free. They took a pipe, to make medicine smoke, and off they went. In the lead was Ma-mi'as-sik-ami, who acted as scout. The others caught birds and small animals for the boy to eat, and at night Coyote and his family lay all round him, and kept him warm. For days and days they travelled. At last, Ma-mi'as-sik-ami told them they were near the den of the Bear. Indeed, they could hear him as he snarled savagely. Se-pe'tso sent his wife to look through a hole in the lodge, so that they might know how the Chinook was kept. But the Bear was very watchful, and when he saw the owl's wife peeking through the hole in his lodge, he took a firestick and hit her in the eye with it. She flew away crying. Se-pe'tso sent his children, one by one. The same thing happened to each of them. Then, he went himself. The Bear poked him with a firestick, too, and he, too, flew away, crying. That is why, even to this day, owls have such big eyes.

"Let me go," said A-pau, the weasel. And he went to the lodge, and peeked through the hole as Se-pe'tso and his family had done. But A-pau, you know, moves very quickly, and, when he saw the Bear look toward the hole, he ducked his head, and the Bear, seeing only his white fur, thought it was just a bit of snow, and he paid no more attention. And A-pau the weasel came back to his friends. "The Bear is huge, and very fierce," he said. "And he has the Chinook tied up in an elkskin bag, at the back of his lodge, farthest from the door. How we can get it, I do not know."

"I shall make a medicine smoke, and blow it into the lodge," said the boy. "It will make the Bear sleepy." So he filled his pipe, and sat down outside the lodge to smoke. He smoked and he smoked. The Bear began to yawn, and nod his head. At last he went to sleep. Then Coyote crept quietly into the lodge, seized the bag with his teeth and dragged it outside. But they could not untie it. And the thongs were tough, too tough for even A-pau's teeth to cut. While they were discussing what to do, they heard a small voice saying, "Ne-sa (brother), let me try." They looked and there was a prairie chicken.

"Very well, little brother," said the boy. The Prairie Chicken flew up on the bag and began to pick out the stitches along the side of it. When only a few of the stitches were broken, the Chinook poured out of the bag, and it began to blow over the country. Snow melted, and water began to run. When the Prairie Chicken flew down to the ground, mud splashed on his feathers . . . and that is why, even to this day, the prairie chicken has spots.

The Bear woke up, and came roaring out of his lodge, and the friends fled. But the Bear could never recapture the Chinook, and, ever since then, bears have slept all winter. And that is why, when they wake up in the spring, they are dreadfully cross. And ever since then, the snow can be deep, and the cold bitter, but, in a short while, the Chinook will come blowing over the mountains, and everyone is happy again.

How the Thunder Made Horses

One fine day, when the Moon of Frogs was rising, Ksis-tse'-kumina, the Thunder, had nothing to do. And he was very bored. He sat up there in the Sky Country, looking about for some way of amusing himself.

Down on the earth he saw a lake, shining in the sunlight. He leaned away over, and reached down to get a big handful of mud out of the middle of it. Then he sat by his fire, making little figures, and baking them in the ashes. When they were well baked, he took them out, and sat idly turning them over and over in his hands. One caught his eye.

"Aie!" said the Thunder, delighted. "Here is something good! Something useful! Maybe pretty, too! I must make this one better, and make more like it!" He threw some more sticks on the fire and reached down into the lake again.

All day long the Thunder worked hard, making horses. He made big ones and little ones, mares and stallions. When he had gotten them all modelled and baked, he lined them up evenly, and looked at them again.

"Sometimes it is cold," he said. "They must have fur, or hair, to keep them warm." But how to get it, and put it on?

Ksis-tse'-kumina looked down to earth again, and his eyes brightened. There were a great many animals down there with the kind of hair he wanted. So he took the hair from the white dogs, from the gophers, from the moose, and the deer, and even the little grey mice, and all these colours of horses he made. Sometimes he had bits of two colours left, and with these he made pintos. Some of the hair fell into the soot by the fire, and that made the black horses.

Ksis-tse'-kumina was very happy. He lined up all the horses he had made, and the lightning went flickering down the row, touching each one in turn, and the little horses came alive, and began to cavort around. Ksis-tse'-kumina sat, smoking his pipe, and watching them. He was very proud of what he had done.

Suddenly, he noticed that his beautiful horses weren't running and jumping any more. They were limping, slowly, and painfully. He had forgotten to make hoofs for them! They had to have hoofs to protect the tender parts of their feet, but what to make them of?

Ksis-tse'-kumina sighed, and set to work to find something that could be made to serve as hoofs. First, he tried making hoofs out of buckskins, like moccasins. These were not bad, but then he thought, "No. These animals will have to travel over rough and stony ground. Moccasins would wear out."

Then he tried making the hoofs out of rock. But the poor little horses limped worse than ever. He tried a lot of other things, but nothing worked. So, up in the Sky Country, Ksis-tse'-kumina sat with his chin on his hand, looking gloomily down to the earth.

Down on the lakeshore, queer little creatures were crawling in the mud. Thunder reached down and snatched a handful of them. And the hoofs of his horses were made from the shells of the turtle. (That, say the Old Ones, is why there are no turtles around this part of the country, now. The Thunder used every one of them for the hoofs of his horses.)

Then the Thunder dropped the horses one by one

down to earth for the Indians to use. And he watches them, even to this day. For if you are cruel to your horses, and run them hard, till they sweat, in a thunderstorm you are likely to lose them. Ksis-tse'-kumina will send lightning to strike them, and take them back to the Sky Country. Ksis-tse'-kumina does not like his gifts to be abused.

"E-ma-ne-ya! True!" say the Old Ones.

The Old Man

One day the Old Man was taking a walk, when he saw a lot of deer playing. They were jumping down a little hill, and having a very good time. Na'pe began crying loudly. Said the leader of the deer to one of the others, "Go and see what Old Man is crying about."

"I am crying because you are having such a good time, and I am not!" said the Old Man. The deer, feeling sorry for him, invited him to join in their game.

He leaped down the hill a few times, then said to the deer chief, "I have been jumping down your hill. Now, since you have been good to me and have let me play with you, I will let you play with me. Come jump down my hill." And he led them to a cutbank!

"I will go first," said Na'pe; but instead of jumping, he ran round to the bottom of the bank, and lay there laughing heartily.

"Why are you laughing?" called the deer, peering over the edge.

"Oh, it is so much fun!" said Na'pe. "The hill is wide; you can all jump at once. Come down here with me!"

So the poor silly deer all jumped at once, and of course, were all killed. Na'pe gleefully skinned them, cut the meat in strips and put it up to dry. He had just finished arranging all the tongues on a long pole, when along came A-pe'si the Coyote. A-pe'si was limping, badly. "Ne-sa (brother)," he said to the Old Man, "I am so hungry. Will you give me some food?"

Na'pe saw that the Coyote was carrying a sea-shell, a

13

big one, hanging on his neck. "Give me that shell, and I will give you some food."

"No," said the Coyote. "I can't give you this shell. It is my Medicine—my power from the Above Spirits—and I should never have good luck again if I gave it away. You have more food here than you need; it will rot before you can use it all. Give me a little."

"No," said Na'pe. "But I will race you for it round this lake. If you win, you may have a meal. If I win, you must give me that holy shell."

"Oh, Ne-sa," said A-pe'si. "Have some pity! I am so lame, and so hungry!"

But Na'pe insisted. At first, he outdistanced the Coyote, but A-pe'si gained, bit by bit, till at last he left Na'pe far behind. When he reached the place where the meat was, he sat down and howled loudly.

At once, all the four-footed animals gathered. Quickly, they ate every single scrap of meat, the mice running up the pole to eat the insides of the tongues. Then they ran away, and hid. And when Na'pe arrived there was not a morsel left, and he was very angry.

But the next time he was not so mean.

The Old Man and the Ducks

One day, when Old Man was walking across the country, he came upon a large lake, on which a great number of ducks were swimming. Na'pe had been walking for some time, and he was hungry. He could have killed with arrows enough ducks for a meal or two, but that was not enough to suit Na'pe. He began making schemes to kill *all* the ducks. Sitting down in some bushes, he thought for a long time. Then he got some clay, and painted his face as did men who had lost a relative in warfare. He crept out of the bushes, and sat down on the lakeshore, where all the ducks could see him, and began crying loudly.

The ducks heard him, and sent one of their number to see what was the trouble. The duck swam in to the shore, and said to the Old Man, "Why are you crying, brother?"

"OW-ooo-ooo!!" howled Na'pe. "I have just come back from a war-party, and all who went with me were killed—my son among them. I want some warriors to go with me and help me to get revenge!"

"Wait here," said the duck, "I will go and tell our chief." And he swam away.

"If our brother is going on a revenge war," said the duck chief, "we must all go with him." And all the ducks swam to the edge of the water, and waddled out on the shore. Na'pe licked his lips.

"Now," he said to the ducks, "you must all line up in a

15

row, and close your eyes tightly. We are going to sing our revenge song, and you must keep your eyes shut till I tell you to open them. Otherwise, we shall have very bad luck. I must feel your hearts, because only the ones with strong hearts may go with us. The weak ones must stay at home."

Na'pe and the ducks all began to sing a revenge song—a war-chant—very loudly. While they were singing, Na'pe went down the line, feeling the ducks' heart-beats. But each one he came to, Na'pe simply wrung its neck!

He had killed a lot of them when an eagle, flying over, saw what he was doing, and cried a warning to the rest of the ducks, who opened their eyes, and quickly flew away, leaving Na'pe screaming with rage. However, he had far more ducks than he could eat, so, after dressing and roasting some of them over his fire, and eating all he could, he put the rest high up in a tree, to have for another day. Then he lay down and went to sleep.

While he was sleeping the eagles came and ate the rest of the ducks.

When Na'pe awakened and found his cache rifled, he made a shocking row. He stamped around, and yelled, and called the eagles vile names. As he was pacing back and forth, he saw in the long reeds by the water's edge some mother ducks, sitting on their nests. He ran toward them, meaning to kill them.

But the eagles were watching. They swooped down, and pulled Na'pe's hair with their claws, pecking him cruelly. "You leave those ducks alone!" said the eagles. "Had it not been for us, you'd have killed all the ducks, and there'd have been none for our children. We were sorry for taking your meat—but now, we are NOT sorry!" And the eagles drove the Old Man away from the place where the ducks lived.

"Oh, well," said Na'pe, on his way, "I had one good meal anyway!'

A Meal for Nata'Yowa

One day, late in the fall, Na'pe was out walking, when he came upon a number of gophers playing near the remains of a camp-fire. It was a raw, cold day, and the gophers were taking turns warming themselves in the ashes of the fire. One gopher would lie down on the ground and the others would cover him with the warm ashes. When he was thoroughly warmed, he would squeak loudly, and another would take his place.

The game gave Na'pe an idea. So, losing no time in carrying out his scheme, he sat down on the ground and began to cry. The gophers came running to see what was the matter.

"Oh, you are having so much fun, getting so nice and warm!" yelled Na'pe. "I am so cold, and there is nobody to play games with me! I wish I could play with you!"

The gophers said, "Well, Old Man, it's not difficult. We do it this way . . ." and the sympathetic gophers invited him into the game. "I will go first," said Na'pe, taking over. "You cover me with the ashes, then, since I am bigger than you I can cover up all of you at once; and we will all be warm at the same time. Then we can do something else."

So Na'pe lay down, and the gophers covered him with ashes, but he had stayed there only a minute when he said he was warm enough, and wished to be let out.

Then it was the turn of the gophers. They all lay down in a neat row, and Na'pe began covering them with ashes. But instead of the just-warm ashes they had been using, Na'pe packed the misguided little animals in hot embers!

The poor gophers squeaked and squealed, but Na'pe, the wicked, just kept piling on hot coals till they were all roasted!

"This will be a very good meal," said Na'pe, going off to the bush for some willow sticks to use in picking up the hot meat.

But while he was gone, along came Nata'Yowa, the Lynx. Nata'Yowa could smell the gophers cooking, and he was hungry. So, losing no time about it, he dug the gophers out of the embers and ate every one of them.

When Na'pe came back, all that was left of his meal was a little pile of tails.

Na'pe was in a fine rage! He danced around furiously. Then, observing a trail which Nata'Yowa had been too full of food and too sleepy to bother hiding, he set off in pursuit of the culprit who had stolen his meat.

Following the trail, he came to where the Lynx was sleeping in the shadow of a large rock. Creeping up, he seized Nata'Yowa by the back of his neck, and began to pound his nose against the rock.

When he had pounded the Lynx's nose till it was very short and stubby Na'pe rubbed his face in the long grass. The grass stuck to Nata'Yowa's face and turned into whiskers. Some of it made little tufts on his ears.

The Old Man picked Nata'Yowa up by his tail, but the tail broke off short. So he took him by the hind legs instead, and twirled Nata'Yowa round his head very rapidly. As he was whirled round, Nata'Yowa's hind legs stretched, till they were longer than they should have been. Then, Na'pe let the Lynx go, and threw him a long way away.

"It serves you right for stealing my food!" said the Old

Man. And that is why Nata'Yowa has a short stubby nose, a bobbed-off tail, whiskers, tufty little ears, and long hind legs.

How the Old Man Made People

L ong ago, when the world was new, there was no one living in it at all, except the Old Man, Na'pe, and his sometimes-friend and sometimes-enemy A-pe'si, the Coyote, and a few buffalo. There were no other people and no other animals. But the Old Man changed all that. He changed it first because he was lonely, and then because he was lazy; and maybe he shouldn't have, but anyway, he did. And this was the way of it.

Na'pe was sitting by his fire one day, trying to think of some way to amuse himself. He had plenty to eat—a whole young buffalo; no need to go hunting. He had a lodge; no work to do; and a fire. He was comfortable, but he wasn't contented. His only companion, A-pe'si the Coyote, was off somewhere on some scheme of his own, and anyway he had quarrelled with A-pe'si, and they were on bad terms; so even if he had been there, Old Man would still have been lonely. He poked some sticks in the fire, threw a rock or two in the river, lit his pipe, and walked around . . . then sat down, and thought how nice it would be to have someone to smoke with, and to talk to. "Another one, like me," he thought. And he poked some more sticks in the fire, and threw some more rocks in the river.

Then he thought, "Why not? I am the Old Man! I can make anything I want to. Why shouldn't I make another like me, and have a companion?" And he promptly went to work.

First, he found a little still pool of water, and looked at

his reflection carefully, so as to know just what he wanted to make. Then he counted his bones as best he could, and felt the shape of them.

Next, he went and got some clay, modelled a lot of bones, and baked them in his fire. When they were all baked, he took them out and looked at them. Some of them were very good, but others were crooked, or too thin, or had broken in the baking. These he put aside in a little heap.

Then he began to assemble the best of the clay bones into a figure of a man. He tied them all together with buffalo sinews, and smoothed them all carefully with buffalo fat. He padded them with clay mixed with buffalo blood, and stretched over the whole thing skin taken from the inside of the buffalo. Then he sat down and lit his pipe again.

He looked at the man he had made rather critically. It wasn't *exactly* what he had wanted, but still it was better than nothing.

"I will make some more," said Na'pe.

He picked the new man up and blew smoke into his eyes, nose, and mouth, and the figure came to life. Na'pe sat him down by the fire, and handed him the pipe. Then he went to get more clay.

All day long Na'pe worked, making men. It took a long time, because some of the bones in each lot weren't good, and he must discard them and make others. But at last he got several men, all sitting by the fire and passing the pipe around. Na'pe sat down with them, and was very happy. He left the heap of discarded bones where they were, at the doorway of his lodge.

So Na'pe and the men lived in his camp, and the men learned to hunt, and Na'pe had company, someone to smoke with, and they were all quite contented.

But the heap of left-over bones was a nuisance. Every time one of the men went in or out of Na'pe's lodge, they tripped over the bones. The wind blew through them at night, making a dreadful noise. The bones frequently tumbled over, making more of a disturbance. Na'pe intended to throw them in the river, but he was a bit lazy, and never got around to it. So the left-over bones stayed where they were.

By this time A-pe-si, the Coyote, was back from wherever he had been. He went around the camp, looking the men over, and being very superior, saying that he didn't think much of Na'pe's handiwork. He was also critical of the heap of bones at the door of the lodge. "I should think you would do something with *them*—make them into men," said A-pe'si, the Coyote.

"All right, I will," said Na'pe. "Only they aren't very good. It will be difficult to make men out of them!"

"Oh, I'll help, I'll help!" said A-pe'si. "With *my* cleverness, we will make something much better than these poor creatures of yours!" So the two of them set to work.

The discarded bones, clicking and rattling, were sorted out, and tied together. Then Na'pe mixed the clay and the buffalo blood to cover them. He fully intended to make the bones into men, but A-pe'si the Coyote kept interfering; consequently, when the job was done, the finished product was quite different. Na'pe surveyed it dubiously, but he blew the smoke into its eyes and nose and mouth, as he had with the men. And the woman came to life.

A-pe'si and Na'pe made the rest of the bones into women, and as they finished each one they put them all together, and the women immediately began to talk to each other.

A-pe'si was very pleased with what *he* had done. "When I made my men," said Na'pe, "I set them down by the fire to smoke."

And even to this day, if you have one group of men, and another of women, the men will want to sit by the fire and smoke. But the women talk. And whether it is because they were made out of the left-over bones that clicked and rattled, or whether it is because A-pe'si, the Coyote—who is a noisy creature himself—had a part in their making, no one can say.

The Eyes of A-pe'si

It happened one hot day when Na'pe, the Old Man, was travelling across the country. This was a long time ago, of course, and in those days enemies were everywhere. To guard against a surprise attack, it was necessary for a traveller to climb tall trees or hills from time to time, and look over the surrounding country.

Old Man was always a bit lazy, and this activity did not appeal to him in the least. He was following a river valley in which there were a large number of birds. And he heard a bird say, "Eyes! Jump over to that tree!" The bird's eyes came out, went up to the top of a dead tree, and looked around. Then the bird said, "Matis! Sa-po-po'ma-ke!" ("Eyes! Come back to me!") and back came his eyes.

Na'pe was greatly intrigued. If he could do that, it would save him any amount of tree-climbing. So he sat down on the ground, and began to cry loudly. Soon the birds gathered to see why Old Man was crying.

"You are having such a good time!" sobbed Na'pe. "I wish I could do that!"

The birds said, "Well, Old Man, it isn't difficult," and then the sympathetic birds told him how to make his eyes come out and fly up to the tops of trees. They warned him, though, that he must only send his eyes up dead trees, and only four times to any one tree.

Na'pe travelled for quite a long time, sending his eyes frequently up trees to see if there were enemies near. But after a while, he got tired, and he lay down to rest, under a very tall, dead tree. He sent his eyes up this tree four times. Then he remembered what the birds had told him. But there were no other dead trees near and Na'pe was too lazy to go and find one. So he said to himself, "Only one time more won't matter!" And he sent his eyes up to the tree-top again. This time, his eyes did not come back when he called them.

Na'pe was furious! He stood at the foot of the tree calling his eyes insulting names. He made such a frightful row that A-pe'si, the Coyote, heard him from a long way off, and came to see what was the trouble. A-pe'si was very happy. The Old Man had more than once plagued *him* and he saw a chance for revenge.

Na'pe at last gave up trying to get back his eyes, and slowly continued his journey. He was having a very bad time finding his way. But other things around helped him. He would bump into a rock or a tree, and ask it, "Are you near the river?" and the rock or tree would tell him where it was, and try to direct his footsteps.

The animals, too, attempted to guide him—all but the Coyote. While Na'pe was inching his way along, the Coyote would creep in front of him—quietly—so that he would trip, and fall. After this happened several times, Na'pe caught the Coyote.

A-pe'si was very frightened. "Ne-sa (brother)," he said, "let me go, and I will take you wherever you want to go."

But Na'pe would not. He took out the Coyote's eye, and put it into his own eye-socket. "Ne-sa, Ne-sa," said the Coyote, "leave one eye for me!" But the Old Man took the Coyote's other eye, too.

Then, because it is a dreadful thing to be blind, the Old Man took two large gooseberries, and put them in the place of the Coyote's eyes. He carefully spat on each one, and then Coyote could see again.

And, the Old Ones say, this is a true story. For, when the dark comes down over the Reservation, and the eyes of A-pe'si shine in the moonlight . . . if you go really close, and look really carefully . . . you will see—they look like gooseberries!

The Snake with the Big Feet

Long ago, in that far-off happy time when the world was new, and there were no white people at all, only Indians and animals, there was a snake who was different from other snakes. He had feet—big feet. And the other snakes, because he was different, hated him, and made life wretched for him. Finally, they drove him away from the country where the snakes lived, saying, "A good long way from here live other ugly creatures with feet like yours. Go and live with them!" And the poor, unhappy Snake had to go away.

For days and days, he travelled. The weather grew cold, and food became hard to find. At last, exhausted, his feet cut and frost-bitten, he lay down on the bank of a river to die.

The Deer, E-se-ko-to-ye, looked out of a willow thicket, and saw the Snake lying on the river bank. Pitying him, the Deer took the Snake into his own lodge and gave him food and medicine for his bleeding feet.

The Deer told the Snake that there were indeed creatures with feet like his who would befriend him, but that some among these would be enemies whom it would be necessary to kill before he could reach safety.

He showed the Snake how to make a shelter for protection from the cold and taught him how to make moccasins of deerskin to protect his feet. And at dawn the Snake continued his journey.

The sun was far down the western sky, and it was bitter cold when the Snake made camp the next night. As he gathered boughs for a shelter, Kaís-kap the porcupine appeared. Shivering, the Porcupine asked him, "Will you give me shelter in your lodge for the night?"

The Snake said, "It's very little that I have, but you are welcome to share it."

"I am grateful," said Kaís-kap, "and perhaps I can do something for you. Those are beautiful moccasins, brother, but they do not match your skin. Take some of my quills, and make a pattern on them, for good luck." So they worked a pattern on the moccasins with the porcupine quills, and the Snake went on his way again.

As the Deer had told him, he met enemies. Three times he was challenged by hostile Indians, and three times he killed his adversary.

At last he met an Indian who greeted him in a friendly manner. The Snake had no gifts for this kindly chief, so he gave him the moccasins. And that, so the Old Ones say, was how our people first learned to make moccasins of deerskin, and to ornament them with porcupine quills in patterns, like those on the back of a snake. And from that day on the Snake lived in the lodge of the chief, counted his coup of scalps with the warriors by the Council fire and, for a long time, was happy.

But the chief had a daughter who was beautiful and kind, and the Snake came to love her very much indeed. He wished that he were human, so that he might marry the maiden, and have his own lodge. He knew there was no hope of this—unless the High Gods, the Above Spirits took pity on him, and would perform a miracle on his behalf.

So he fasted and prayed for many, many days. But all his fasting and praying had no result, and at last the Snake became very ill.

Now, in the tribe, there was a very highly skilled

medicine man. Mo'ki-ya was an old man, so old that he
had seen and known, and understood, everything that
came within the compass of his people's lives, and many
things that concerned the Spirits. Many times, his lodge
was seen to sway with the Ghost Wind, and the voices of
those long gone on to the Sand Hills spoke to him.

Mo'ki-ya came to where the Snake lay in the chief's
lodge, and sending all the others away, asked the Snake
what his trouble was.

"It is beyond even your magic," said the Snake, but he
told Mo'ki-ya about his love for the maiden, and his
desire to become a man so that he could marry her.

Mo'ki-ya sat quietly thinking for a while. Then he
said, "I shall go on a journey, brother. Perhaps my
magic can help, perhaps not. We shall see when I
return." And he gathered his medicine bundles and
disappeared.

It was a long and fearsome journey that Mo'ki-ya
made. He went to the shores of a great lake. He climbed
a high mountain, and he took the matter to Nato'se, the
Sun himself.

And Nato'se listened, for this man stood high in the regard of the Spirits, and his medicine was good. He did
not ask, and never had asked, for anything for himself,
and to transform the Snake into a brave of the tribe was
not a difficult task for the High Gods.

The third day after the arrival of Mo'ki-ya at the Sun's
abode, Nato'se said to him, "Return to your own lodge,
Mo'ki-ya, and build a fire of small sticks. Put many
handfuls of sweet-grass on the fire, and when the smoke
rises thickly, lay the body of the Snake in the middle of
it."

And Mo'ki-ya came back to his own land.

The fire was built in the centre of the medicine lodge,

as the Sun had directed, and when the sweet-grass smouldered among the embers, sending the smoke rolling in great billows through the tepee, Mo'ki-ya gently lifted the Snake, now very nearly dead, and placed him in the fire so that he was hidden by the smoke.

The medicine-drum whispered softly in the dusk of the lodge: the chant of the old men grew a little louder, and then the smoke obscuring the fire parted like a curtain, and a young man stepped out.

Great were the rejoicings in the camp that night. The Snake, now a handsome young brave, was welcomed into the tribe with the ceremonies befitting the reception of one shown to be high in the favour of the Spirits. The chief gladly gave him his daughter, happy to have a son-in-law of such distinction.

Many brave sons and beautiful daughters blessed the lodge of the Snake and at last, so the Old Ones say, his family became a new tribe—the Pek-sik-siné-ta-pe, or Snake Indians.

The Girl Who Married the Morning Star

On a hot summer night, in a long-ago time, three young girls were lying on the grass by the river, talking, as young girls do, of the men they would marry some day. One daughter of a chief, the most beautiful of the three, found fault with every man suggested by the others. At last exasperated, they said to her, "What do you want for husband—a star? No man pleases you!"

The girl raised her eyes to the sky, where one star shone brighter than all the rest. "I would marry that star if he would come and get me. I wish he would! Please come, Star!!" The girls laughed, and returned to their tepees.

When night came again, there was need of wood, to feed the camp-fires, and the girls were sent to gather some.

While they were picking up the dried branches, a young man dressed in beautiful feathered garments stepped out of a thicket, and said to the daughter of the chief, "Are you ready to go?"

"Go? Go where?" she said. "Who are you?"

"I am the Star you called last night," the stranger said. "You offered to marry me, remember? I have come to take you to my home in the Sky Country."

The girl looked at him. He was tall, and strong, and his eyes were kind. She turned to her companions, and said to them, "Tell my parents where I have gone." And the other girls, frightened, ran toward the camp.

The Star Man took a robe, made of feathers, and

coloured like the rainbow, from his back, and, wrapping it round the girl, held her close against him. And they rose through the air toward the Sky Country.

It was a beautiful country. There was green grass, and flowers, and berries and quiet-running water. There was neither sickness, nor pain; the lodges never wore out, nor the clothing; there was always food, just by wishing for it—and the winter never came. The women had only to do what work they wished, and the men spent all their time on raids, and war. But those who were killed always, by daylight next morning, were alive again. And the animals were tame, and easy to hunt. It was a beautiful country.

The girl forgot all about her people and her life on the earth. After a while a son was born to them, and her happiness was complete.

Only one thing was forbidden. Her husband had told her that never was she to pull up a certain large wild turnip (ma'as) that grew in a hollow near their tepee. For a long time she respected the restriction, but more and more she wondered, Why? What would happen if she did? The thought grew, and grew.

One day her husband went hunting; and as she sat in the tepee with nothing to do, she thought of the ma'as. And she went to the hollow and pulled it up.

The ma'as left a hole in the sky, and looking down through it, she saw a circle of lodges, with the people going about the daily tasks of the camp. A wave of homesickness poured over her—a nostalgia for the life she had left, for the gossip of the women, the familiar tasks, the noise and smells of the camp. She replaced the ma'as, and went, weeping, to her lodge.

Her husband, returning, found her sobbing in the tepee. "You disobeyed me," he said, sadly. "Now, I must send you back to your people." He sent messengers to gather hides of buffalo, hundreds of them, all the Star people had. Then they cut each hide into long strips, and tied them together, making a long, long rope.

They lowered the girl and her baby down to the earth. But the baby was changed into a large mushroom, or puff-ball (which our people call "Star-Balls") since, being a sky-child, he could not live on the earth.

With her the girl also brought the Sacred Turnip, the ma'as, and on her head she wore the holy Crown, the head-dress used to this day by the woman who makes the Sun Dance. (And to this day, the ma'as has a part in those rituals, and the poles of the Sun Lodge are tied with rawhide rope.)

The girl lived with her family, teaching the people much that she had learned in the Sky Country. She tended her Star baby.

But among the people were some who resented her teaching. And one day, these wicked ones took the Star baby, and cut it up into small pieces, and scattered the bits around on the ground.

The girl was heartbroken at the killing of her Star baby. When the Morning Star rose next, she went out on the prairie and called to her husband, asking him if the ones who did this could not be punished.

He answered her, and told her to have her father and other men build a raft of logs tied with thongs. When the raft was completed, they were to take a pair of each kind of animal on to the raft, and to warn the virtuous members of her tribe to go there too.

Then the Star sent moon after moon of rain, till all the earth was flooded. The people and animals on the raft were all that were left alive.

When the rain had ceased, the girl's father sent a

young beaver to find land. The beaver never came back.

Later, the chief sent a duck out. The duck, too, did not return. He sent other birds, and other water animals, and they, also, were not seen again.

At last, the muskrat said, "Let me go." The chief protested. He was fond of the muskrat, and the others had not come back. But the girl added her voice to that of the muskrat and at last the chief consented, and the little animal departed.

Late in the night, a feeble splashing was heard alongside the raft. The muskrat, nearly dead from exhaustion, had come back, and clutched in one little paw was a tiny bit of earth.

The water was receding, and at last the green grass grew again, and the flood was over. (The water went into the rivers, and the lakes, and down into holes and crevices in the ground. That's why, when you dig a well, you get water.)

The girl saw her people happy again, leading lives of virtue, with due attention given to the things she had taught them. But she was lonely, and when the Morning Star shone bright, she went out and called him, and the Star Man came for her as he had before, and they went back to their home in the Sky Country.

The Moon Woman

Long ago the Moon Woman was an Indian girl, the beautiful daughter of a great chief. She loved a young warrior of the tribe, and he loved her; but he was an orphan and poor, and had no goods wherewith to pay the bride price the old chief demanded from the man who would wed his daughter. Hoping to acquire the wealth he needed he left with a war-party, to be gone for many moons.

While he was absent, a wealthy war chief, a much older man, came to the maiden's father with an offer of many horses, many robes, and other valuables.

Her father accepted them, and, though the maiden pleaded, and struggled, she was taken to the old war chief's tepee, and made his wife.

The war chief was kind to her, and nothing was spared to make her happy, but she only wept, and grew more frail day by day. At last, a son was born to them, and the old chief thought that surely, now, she would be content; but still she grieved, and in a short time, she died.

Her husband was heartbroken—for he *had* loved her. He put her body in his own tepee, with the most valued of his possessions, and he bound the lodge with rawhide rope so that her spirit could not leave.

For three days and three nights he stayed there, pleading with her spirit to return to her body, and mourning for her. At the end of that time his friends came and took him away with them, and the tepee was left, standing alone on the prairie. But the young warrior remained behind when the rest moved away. And after a while, he went to the tepee and spoke to the dead girl. He told her all his love, and his loneliness for her; and her spirit answered him. When he touched her hand it moved and warmed, and then she was alive again.

The young warrior was happy, though he knew well that in reality his sweetheart was a ghost-woman, and might leave him at any time. They lived together for a long while, but at last the woman remembered that she had a son, and she took a great longing to see the child.

The warrior tried to dissuade her, but she would not listen. She coaxed him to take her to the camps of their people. He protested that no good would come of it, but she insisted, and they went. He made only one condition—that she disguise herself as a man, so that her husband would not recognize her.

This she did, but when they were in the camp, in her husband's lodge, she betrayed herself by some feminine gesture. With a shout her husband attempted to seize her. Hemmed in, she could not escape through the doorway of the lodge, so, snatching up her son, she jumped toward the opening at the top of the tepee. The old war chief slashed at her with his stone axe, but she was beyond his reach, though he cut off part of one leg. She dropped the child, but she herself escaped.

The Sky People were sorry for her, and sent a flight of eagles to bring her up into the Sky Country, where she was given a home in the moon.

And all you have to do is to look at the face of the full moon. She is an old, old woman, now, but she is there, to this day.

And there is no doubt about *who* it is, either—for the woman in the moon has only one leg.

The Ghost Stallion

This is a tale the old men tell around the tepee fire, when the stars are blown clean on a windy night, and the coyotes are howling on the Cree Jump. And when, sometimes, over the wind, comes clearly the sound of running horses, their hearers move a little closer to one another—and pile more wood on the fire.

This is a story from a long time ago, say the Old Ones. What the man's name was, no one knows now, and so they call him "The Traveller."

Long ago, The Traveller was a wealthy chief. A warrior in his young days, he had taken many scalps, many horses, many another trophy of value. And he had increased his possessions by hard dealings with those less fortunate, and by gambling with younger men who were no match for his cunning.

He was not loved by his fellow-tribesmen—though they admired his bravery—for in times of hardship, when other chiefs shared freely whatever they had, he drove hard bargains, and generally prospered from the ills of others. His wives he had abused till their parents took them away; his children hated him, and he had no love for them.

There was only one thing he cared for—his horses. They were fine horses, beautiful horses, for he kept only the best, and when a young warrior returned from a raid with a particularly good horse, The Traveller never rested until (whether by fair means or not) he had it in his possession.

At night, when the dance drum was brought out, and the other Indians gathered round it, The Traveller went alone to the place where his horses were picketed, to gloat over his treasures. He loved them. But he loved only the ones that were young, and handsome, and healthy; a horse that was old, or sick, or injured, received only abuse.

One morning, when he went to the little valley in which his horses were kept, he found in the herd an ugly white stallion. He was old, with crooked legs, and a matted coat, thin, and tired-looking.

The Traveller flew into a rage. He took his rawhide rope, and caught the poor old horse. Then, with a club, he beat him unmercifully. When the animal fell to the ground, stunned, The Traveller broke his legs with the club, and left him to die. He returned to his lodge, feeling not the slightest remorse for his cruelty.

Later, deciding he might as well have the hide of the old horse, he returned to the place where he had left him. But, to his surprise, the white stallion was gone.

That night, as The Traveller slept, he had a dream. The white stallion appeared to him, and slowly turned into a beautiful horse, shining white, with long mane and tail—a horse more lovely than any The Traveller had ever seen.

Then the Stallion spoke: "If you had treated me kindly," it said, "I would have brought you more horses. You were cruel to me, so I shall take away the horses you have!"

When The Traveller awoke, he found his horses were gone. All that day, he walked and searched, but when at nightfall he fell asleep exhausted, he had found no trace of them. In his dreams, the White Stallion came again, and said, "Do you wish to find your horses? They are north, by a lake. You will sleep twice, before you come to it."

As soon as he awakened in the morning, The Traveller hastened northward. Two days' journey, and when he came to the lake there were no horses.

That night, the Ghost Stallion came again. "Do you wish to find your horses?" it said. "They are east, in some hills. There will be two sleeps before you come to the place."

When the sun had gone down on the third day, The Traveller had searched the hills, but had found no horses. And so it went; night after night the Stallion came to The Traveller, directing him to some distant spot, but he never found his horses. He grew thin, and footsore. Sometimes he got a horse from some friendly camp, sometimes he stole one, in the night. But always, before morning, would come a loud drumming of hoofs, the Ghost Stallion and his band would gallop by, and the horse of The Traveller would break its picket, and go with them.

And never again did he have a horse; never again did he see his own lodge. And he wanders, even to this day, the old men say, still searching for his lost horses.

Sometimes, they say, on a windy autumn night when the stars shine very clearly, and over on the Cree Jump the coyotes howl, above the wind you may hear a rush of running horses, and the stumbling footsteps of an old man. And, if you are very unlucky, you may see the Stallion and his band—and The Traveller, still pursuing them, still trying to get back his beautiful horses.

The Ghost Pipe

The man was young, and strong, a warrior, and a hunter. The Old Ones of the tribe looked at him with approval, and there was no maiden who would not gladly have been his wife. But when the time came for him to choose a woman to sit beside him, he did not take one of the tall, confident ones. The girl he chose was small, and frail, and had been hurt in her childhood so that she could not walk without limping.

The Old Ones of the Council were angry. They said, "This is no woman for you, this cripple! What sons will she give you? Choose another!" And to each other they said, "Why? She is not even pretty!"

But the man saw laughter in her eyes, and he heard music in her voice, and he said to the Old Ones, "I will have this woman—or none!"

And because he was a very great warrior, the Old Ones said, "Ah, well, he will tire of her soon. He will take other wives, and there will be sons for the war-trails."

So the man took the woman to his tepee. In their lodge there was always laughter. When others were present, he treated her as other men treated their wives, and she was silent and obedient. But when they were alone they talked and laughed, and sometimes, when the moon was bright, they would sit by the river, and she would sing songs for him—about the water spirits, and the night birds. And it seemed to the man that the river sang with her.

The woman had a fear of storms. When Ksis-tse'-

kumina, the Thunder, came walking over the mountains, she covered her head with her robe, and shivered, and wept. And the man held her close, comforting her, and laughed at her gently when the storm went down.

Now he was a hunter, and a very great warrior, and absent often on war-party, or hunting expedition. The Old Ones waited in vain for the other wives they had thought he would take—and there were no sons for the war-trails.

Then when the Moon of Flying Birds was rising, the man left with a war-party; and while he was away, the woman became ill, and died. Returning homeward, he saw the death-fires burning in the valley. He heard the chanting, and the wailing of women; and seeing all the others there, he knew it was his who had gone.

There was no comfort for him. The Old Ones, pleased, said, "Ah, he will soon forget her! He will marry a strong woman, and there will be sons for the war-trails!"

But he looked at the other women, and hated them for being alive when she was dead. Sometimes he would waken from a dream, thinking he heard her call. Only when the thunder rolled and crashed over the mountains did the pain in his heart ease a little, knowing how she had feared it, and glad it would frighten her no longer.

On raids, and in battles, he was reckless, for he had no wish to live; but the death he sought evaded him, and in the camps he walked alone.

So the year came round again to the Moon of Flying Birds—and the man had not forgotten. Since he was a warrior, a brave man, he resolved to go where only the dead had gone before, to take the East Road, the trail to the Sand Hills, the abode of the dead. There he would seek his wife, and if the spirits, the guardians of the place would not give her back to him, he would remain with her.

The East Road is three days long, so the Old Ones say. Three days the ghosts of the dead must travel before they come to the Sand Hills.

The man travelled for three days, and when he had passed the tall trees that mark the end of the road, he heard a woman's voice say, "There are children playing at your feet. Don't tread on them!"

The man reached down to his feet. He felt nothing, and he saw nothing, but a child laughed, suddenly, and he knew he was in the country of the dead. The voice spoke again. "You are not one of us," it said. "Why have you come here?"

"I have come to find a woman," he said.

"In your world there are many women," said the sweet voice. "Must you come to the land of the dead for one?"

"Aie, my sister," said the man, "there are none like the one I seek. Take your children away from my feet, now. I must find the chiefs of this place, and tell them why I am here."

"There is a lodge a little farther on," said the voice. "Go in and wait."

The lodge was large, painted with strange symbols. The man went in, and found it empty, except for a pipe filled with kínikínik, and lighted.

The pipe was lifted suddenly and began to circle the lodge as if it were being passed from hand to hand, and when it had made the circuit four times the figures of a chief and his council appeared.

The Ghost Chief asked what had brought the man there.

43

"I have come for my wife," said the man. "She died in the Moon of Flying Birds, and without her, my lodge is cold. And for me, the summer never comes."

"In the lodges of the Siksika there are many women," said the Ghost Chief. "Is there only this one for you?"

The man turned his head so that his eyes met the eyes of the Ghost Chief. And he said, "There is only this one!"

The Ghost Chief smiled. "Is she so beautiful?"

"She is small," said the man, hesitating, "and thin, and lame. But her eyes have laughter in them, and her voice is like small rivers running."

The Ghost Chief sat in silence a while; then he rose, and gave an order to one of his council. "We are many, here," he said, "and our moons are not the same as yours. The women will come, and yours will be somewhere among them."

Soon, the sound of women's voices filled the lodge. The Ghost Pipe circled four times again, and the women became visible. The man scanned their ranks eagerly, but the one he sought was not there.

The Ghost Chief dismissed the women, and sent another of his council for the women who had died in another moon. Again the voices of women, and again the circling pipe—but again she was not there. Not till the last group of women came did she appear. He had feared that she might have changed in the Spirit World, but she had not. The Ghost Chief dismissed the other women, and the man, with his ghost-wife, stood facing the council.

Then one of the council spoke to the Ghost Chief. He said, "Does the woman wish to return to the lodge of her husband? For in their world there is pain, and too much fear, and here there is neither."

The Ghost Chief spoke to the woman. "You have heard the Councillor. Do you want to go back?"

The woman looked at her husband, and answered the ghosts, "In that other world, it is true there is fear, and pain—but the pain I have lived with, and I feared only the storms. I will go back."

The Ghost Chief said to the man, "The woman will return. But are you sure that is what you wish? The man who lives with a ghost-woman takes no other wife. And you will have no children, no sons for the war-trails. You will have only this one woman!"

"*This one woman,*" said the man, with anger, "I will love till I die—and after! Other women I do not want . . . and other men may have the sons for the war-trails!"

"A day will come," said the Ghost Chief, "when you will wish you had not done this. You could love another woman; you could envy another man his sons . . . And when that day comes, remember this—you must never strike this ghost-woman. You must never taunt her with the fact that she is a ghost, is not like other women."

"I will remember," said the man.

The Ghost Chief turned to the woman. "A man who can love a woman enough to follow her to the place of the dead, and a woman who can be so loved, are worthy of a gift," he said. "This pipe I will send with you. The woman will carry it, and will walk behind you. If you so much as turn your head to look at her, before you reach the camps of your people, she will be back here, in the Sand Hills. When you come in sight of your camp, stop and wait. Your people will send a runner out to see who you are, and what you want. Tell the messenger to have four sweat-baths prepared. Take coloured clays, and paint them, red on one side for the daylight, black on the other for the night. Bathe in each one, in turn. This will wash away all trace of the Spirit World, and you can live with your own people again."

And to the woman he said, "Take this. It will control the storms you fear. It will warn you of war, and trouble. And when one you love dies, the pipe will tell you. It will be a comfort to you, and to your people, and a reminder, forever, of this journey."

So the man and woman began the long journey back to their own world. And because he could not look at her, the woman sang, so that he would know she was there. Then, when the sun had risen and set three times, they saw the shining white mountains rise ahead of them, and they knew the journey was ending.

On a hill overlooking the camps, they stopped and waited. Soon a runner was sent out to see who and what they were. There was great rejoicing at the return of the man, for he had been mourned as dead. And the woman? The Old Ones muttered, for now there was no hope of other wives, and the healthy sons they had hoped for. But the children welcomed her, and other women looked at her with envy, for no one of them had been so beloved.

The baths were prepared, and the man and woman bathed, as the Ghost Chief had directed. Then they went to their own tepee, and lived as they had before. And in their lodge there was always laughter.

The years went on, and the man and the woman grew old. And sometimes, the man sat by the fires when the young men were telling their adventures, and counting their coups . . . and sometimes he wished that he might have had sons like them. And, sometimes, a woman walked near him . . . and in his mind he heard the Ghost Chief say, "The man who lives with a ghost-woman takes no other wife!"

And so a day came. The council of chiefs met in the man's lodge. The woman was hurrying back and forth preparing food and making ready to receive the guests. And she angered her husband. Roughly, he pushed her out of his way, shouting, "You behave like a ghost!"

Then his heart chilled. A dark shadow moved across her face. Just for a moment it lifted, and he saw that she was young again, as when he had gone to the Sand Hills for her. She smiled at him, and the darkness came over her face again. Then she vanished, and he knew she had returned to the land of the dead.

And he forgot that he had coveted other men's sons, other men's women. His heart ached as it had the first time she went away. He sat with his head bowed, and when the Old Ones came, he sent them away, saying, "I must prepare for a journey."

And the Old Ones, knowing what he meant, went away, and sent boys to gather wood for the death-fires. Late in the night, the man began his journey to the Sand Hills.

The death-fires burned behind him. The wailing of women, and the old chants followed him down the East Road. And after a while a voice spoke to him out of the shadows. "I waited for you," she said. He took her hand, and they laughed, and went on their way to the Sand Hills.

And back in the camps of their people the Old Ones sighed and shook their heads. "He should have had sons for the war-trails," they said.

But they wrapped the pipe and kept it carefully, and our people have it to this day.

And when Ksis-tse'-kumina, the Thunder, comes walking over the mountains, with a sound like giant dance drums, and the lightning glares, and flickers across the Reservation, old men unwrap the Pipe, and the storm dies away. When war, or trouble threaten, the Pipe talks, warning.

But when a loved one dies, the Pipe sings with a strange comfort . . . for the beloved dead can never be lost to us in the way that the living can be lost; for them there is no more pain, and no more fear. And the East Road is only three days long: they are not far away.

The Story of the Sun Dance

In a long-ago time there lived in the camps of the Siksika a girl who was lovely beyond belief. The only daughter of a great war chief, the best the Indian life afforded was for her. But she was kind, and gentle, and beloved by the people of her tribe. She was valued, too, by the old chief, her father, who expected her beauty to bring him much in the way of goods from the man who would be her husband. Perhaps he hoped, too, for a son-in-law to boast of—some great warrior, to count coup in the Council when he himself was too old for the war-trails.

But to all the warriors, the braves of the tribe who sought to marry her, she said no. To the chiefs, who came from other tribes with offers of many horses, many robes, she said no. Her father, at last, was angered. He demanded to know why she had refused these fine offers.

"I belong to the Sun," said the maiden. "I will marry none of these men!"

"What would the Sun want of an earth maiden?" scoffed her father. "I shall choose your husband myself, then!" and though the maiden wept, and pleaded, he would not listen.

That night, as the old chief slept, Nato'se, the Sun himself, came to him in a dream. "The maiden is mine," Nato'se said. "And I will not have her troubled! She will have a husband, but *I* will choose him, when the right time comes."

So the girl was no longer urged to marry, and was

treated throughout the camp with the reverence due a holy person.

Now in this camp there was also living a young man, whose parents had died when he was very young. The men of the Siksika walk tall and straight—then, as now—and they had small sympathy for this orphan, for he was a little man with a crooked back, and a face so marred and twisted that children ran from him, and women turned away. So little did they regard him, that he had not even a name—they called him "Scarface."

His deformity made him an outcast, the butt of ridicule, the object of torment; and to the men and boys of the camp, whatever added to the misery of this poor creature, or deepened the pain he suffered, was accounted fine sport. The men would not let him hunt with them, and often they robbed him of what few animals he could manage to trap. Hunger, and cold, pain, and bitter humiliation were his constant companions.

Sometimes at night when the moon was full, when the aching of his heart and body would not let him sleep, he would wander far out on the prairie. And it seemed to him that the Moon Woman listened when he prayed; and he thought of her as the mother he had never known and the sweetheart he could never have. And always he hoped for the dream-vision, the coming of the medicine, or dream-power which would put an end to his persecution.

But though he waited and fasted and prayed, the vision never came. And in all the camps of the Siksika, only two people were kind to him—an old medicine woman, and the Sun Maiden. The old woman made him clothing, and taught him sacred chants and prayers. The Sun Maiden spoke to him gently, had food given to him, and tried, at least, to make the others kinder. And as time went on she came to see in this poor outcast a fine mind, and a gentle heart; and a quiet endurance of torture that daily surpassed what the braves who despised him prided themselves upon enduring once in a lifetime.

But her kindness and understanding added to his torment. For a little man—lame, and twisted, and ugly—has the same emotions, the same feelings, as the ones who walk tall and straight. He feels pain, and cold, and hunger. He can be as lonely. He can love a woman just as much as other men.

And so poor Scarface came to love the Sun Girl. Soon, others noted his devotion, and the life which had been wretched became unbearable. Scarface knew he must leave the camp. But first, he would tell the Sun Girl of his love for her, and have at least the poor satisfaction of knowing that she understood his feeling.

"I belong to the Sun," said the maiden, "but he said that he would one day choose a husband for me. It may be that if you could find your way to the Sky Country, he would take the scars from your face and let you marry me. Go to the Sun."

He asked the old medicine woman how to find the home of the Sun.

"I do not know the way," said the old woman, "except that you must travel east for many moons. But I know that you will find those that will help you. All I can do is to prepare the food and the moccasins you will need for your journey." And this she did.

So Scarface began his journey to the Sun. Many, many days he travelled. His moccasins were ragged, and his food was gone before he met the Wolf.

"Tell me the way to the lodge of the Sun, brother!" he said to the Wolf.

"East of here, little brother!" said the Wolf. "Where,

and how far, I do not know, but the Bear is older than I, and wiser, and it may be that he knows. Ask the Bear!"

Scarface travelled on eastward. Many days later, he met the Bear.

"Tell me the way to the lodge of the Sun, brother!" he said to the Bear.

"East of here, little brother!" said the Bear. "Where, and how far, I do not know, but the Beaver has powerful medicine, and it may be that he knows. Find the Beaver!"

Travelling farther east, Scarface met the Beaver.

"Tell me the way to the lodge of the Sun, brother!" he begged the Beaver.

"East of here, little brother," said the Beaver. "The Black Fox knows. Ask the Black Fox!"

Scarface found the Black Fox and repeated the inquiry. The Black Fox guided him to a great body of water. "Across this water," said the Fox, "the lodge of Nato'se stands. Lie down now, and sleep, and a way will come for you to cross to it." And the Fox turned and left him alone.

Far away, to the westward, the Sun was disappearing. Scarface lifted his arms to the sunset, and prayed. Then, exhausted, he lay down, and slept.

Now as he slept, the dream-vision he had so long awaited came to him. The cool light of the full moon surrounded him, and a beautiful woman appeared—the Moon Woman.

"Who are you?" she said, "and why are you here?"

"I have come many moons from my own land," said Scarface, "and in my own land I am an outcast. You see my face—and my body. . . . The men of my tribe walk tall, and straight, and with them there is no place for one like me. I seek the lodge of the Sun, for I love a maiden who belongs to him. I hope he will help me; but if he will not, I die as easily here as in the camps of my people."

"I have a son," said the Moon Woman, "and he has need of a friend, a companion. A road will appear to you across the water. Don't be afraid to walk on it. It will lead you to the Sky Country, and the lodge of the Sun."

Scarface awakened, and the moon-track lay gold on the water. A little way off the Black Fox barked, and the night birds swooped and called. He walked out on the moon-track. It was smooth and safe, and he followed it across the water.

It was a beautiful country he found there. Beside the trail lay all manner of things treasured by Indians— robes, and war-gear, strange garments embroidered with feathers, medicine pipes, and drums—but he walked past without touching them.

A young man, tall and handsome, came toward him. "I am the Morning Star," he said. "I will take you to the lodge of my father, the Sun. My father and mother are waiting for us."

The two young men walked toward the lodge of the Sun. Suddenly a great voice called to them. "Who comes to the lodge of Nato'se?"

"A man from the earth-people," said Morning Star. "He will be my friend."

"Walk naked! Walk naked!" said the Sun. "My lodge must not be tainted with the garments of men!"

The rags of Scarface and the beautiful clothing of Morning Star were left beside the trail, and the young men approached the lodge, from which the fragrant smoke of burning sweet-grass was rising.

"I have expected you," said the Sun to Scarface.

"Long ago, I chose you for the husband of my adopted daughter, the Sun Maiden. And I marked you, for you must have the knowledge that comes from suffering. You were brave in coming here, and now the time has come to make you what I intend you shall be."

And he arose, and came to Scarface. With his hands, Nato'se kneaded the spine of the man, till he stood erect and straight. Then he said to his own son, and Scarface, "Go out, and build four sweat-lodges. Place them in a row, east to west. Paint one-half of each red, for the daylight, and half black, for the night. Make a square hole in the floor of each where we can place the stones." And the lodges were built.

The Moon made the fire, and heated the stones. Sun, Morning Star and Scarface entered the first lodge. The Sun seated himself on the south side facing the centre, Scarface on his left, Morning Star on his right. Burning embers were placed at each side of the hole which had been made in the floor of the lodge, and sweet-grass was burned on the embers. The Moon brought in the hot stones, then gave her husband his pipe, and the three smoked while the incense burned. A bowl of water was brought in, then the Moon drew the hides covering the lodge together, so that it was dark inside.

The Sun began to sing, as he poured the water on the hot stones, and when the steam rose thickly he called to the Moon, telling her to lift the covering of the lodge and let the light in. Moon lifted the cover at the east side of the lodge and closed it again. When the steam thickened, she opened the cover at the west side of the lodge. This was done four times, and when the Sun had completed his songs they left the lodge.

Three times more, in the three remaining lodges, the ceremony was repeated, and when the three emerged from the last lodge the scars were gone, and Scarface was as straight and handsome as Morning Star.

"Now," said the Sun, "there are things I must teach you, rituals I want you to learn, knowledge to take back to earth with you." He took Scarface to the edge of the Sky Country, and together they looked down at the earth.

"It is mine," said the Sun. "Without my power, nothing can live. And I am to be honoured, and respected. Food comes from me and light and warmth, and healing; and all things that are beautiful, and courage, and love. And all these things I will give, in answer to the prayers of my people. And the way of your praying must be thus: build me a lodge, round, like the Sun and the full moon, with arched sticks. Paint half red for the daylight, half black, for the night.

"Remember the things I value: a virtuous woman, a buffalo robe, fur of the beaver, feathers of the eagle, the sign of my lodge, the tongue of the buffalo. All these things I find pleasing, and when they accompany your prayers, I will answer them."

For many moons, Scarface dwelt in the land of the Sun, and all the wisdom of the Sky People he learned.

Then the Wolf Road shone white across the sky, and the seven Wolves—the stars of the dipper—stood guard, as Scarface came down the Wolf Road, and back to earth.

He found the camps of his people, and they, forgetting the contempt they had once had for him, welcomed him.

The Sun Maiden was his, and together they established the rituals of the Sun Dance. Many things they taught the Indian people, and when their work was done they went back to the Sky Country.

And to this day the rites of O-kan, the Sun Dance, are

performed as Scarface taught, and each year, when the Moon of Berries shines, the journey of Scarface to the lodge of the Sun is acted over again.

And the men of the Siksika walk tall and straight. But to the crippled, the twisted, the scarred—to all who are not like their fellow-men—they are kind and gentle. And if you ask them why, they will tell you, "It is because of Scarface. Because Scarface was a little man—with a crooked back, and a face so hideous that children ran from him. And it was he who brought the wisdom of the Sun to our people."

The Wood Cree's Story

A long time ago, the Old Ones say, in the Moon of Frogs, a stranger came to the camps of our people. He built a lodge, and he stayed. He was a Wood Cree, a gentle, soft-speaking man, and for that some among the young men thought him timid. But the Old Ones looked at his body, and they looked at his hands, and they knew. No coward bears marks like the ones he bore. He hunted with our men, and he was a good hunter. At night he sat by our fires, but he counted no coups—brave deeds and adventures—and he sang no songs. He brought no woman with him, and he took none from among us. After a while, the people began to whisper about him.

Old Ones know that the noisy are not always the brave, that often courage will sit in silence, but the young men have that to learn. So our guest was taunted, covertly at first; then, when he seemed not to notice, more openly. The Old Ones themselves whispered that strange voices and an odd, sweet song were heard from his lodge in the dead of the night. Our people began to avoid the Wood Cree and to wish that he would go away. Then, one night, he told them a story.

"When I was a young man," he said, "I had a wife and a child. One year, when the Moon of Frogs was rising, we moved away from the rest of our people to hunt. It had been bad that winter—cold and stormy. The buffalo had gone far away, and we had been hungry.

"We went west toward the mountains, where the deer were, and the buffalo might be. Toward nightfall we made camp. I found a deer and killed it. While our daughter slept in the lodge, my wife and I dressed the animal and brought it home to our camp.

"We went to wake our daughter so that she might eat with us, but she was not there. We could not find her anywhere. We called and searched, and after a while we lay down, too tired to search uselessly in the dark.

"Then we heard a child crying and we jumped up and searched again. The crying seemed to come from under the robes we had spread on the ground. We moved them, but found no child, though the crying continued. We dug away the turf, and there were the bones of a woman. Suddenly, a woman's voice wailed in the tepee, and our child was where we had left her.

" 'Let us take our baby, and go away from this place!' said my wife.

" 'We cannot move camp in the dark in a strange place,' I said. 'Wait till morning.' And we lay down to sleep. Then the wailing came again and a woman's voice spoke. 'Give me the child!' it said. 'Give me the child!'

" 'Who are you?' we asked.

" 'I am the ghost of the woman whose bones you disturbed,' she said. 'When I was alive, I had no child. My husband was a warrior, a great man, and kind to me. I loved him, but we had no child. Other wives had sons for him, daughters for him, but I had none. Give me this child—it is only a girl—and I will reward you.'

" 'No,' I said. 'We could not give away our child to a ghost. Besides, what could you do to reward me?'

" 'Ghosts have great power,' she said. 'Give me the child, and I will protect you in battle, shield you in raids.

Give me the child and I will make you the greatest of war chiefs.'

" 'No!' said my wife.

" 'Be quiet,' I said to her.

" 'Give me the child!' said the ghost-woman. 'Give me the child and I will bring you the buffalo. I will make you the greatest of hunters!'

" 'No!' said my wife, and she held the girl close to her. 'Will you be quiet?' I said.

" 'Give me the child,' said the ghost-woman, 'and I will give you powerful medicine. All the tribes will know you.'

" 'It is true,' I said. 'It is only a girl-child. I will have many others, and sons.'

" 'Give me the child,' said the ghost-woman, 'and I will be a second wife to you—a servant in your lodge. I will make you beautiful clothing, prepare your food. You will not see me, but whatever you wish will be done.'

" 'No!' said my wife, wailing.

" 'Be quiet!' I said, and I struck her.

" 'Give me the child!' said the ghost-woman.

"And I gave her the child.

"My wife wept. After a while she rose and went out of the lodge. She did not come back.

"Late in the night a woman (I thought my wife) came into the tepee, and crept in beside me. I held her close, loving her. Before morning, the woman moved in my arms, and was bones, and was gone. Then I knew. It was the ghost-woman.

"You know, the man who takes a ghost-woman takes no other, ever. He has no child, no son, no daughter, ever. The ghost-woman kept her promises. But my people said I was *Wendigo,* and I went away from them.

And that ghost-wife is with me still."

That is the story the Old Ones say he told them. And they say that when he ended the story they heard a woman's voice call him, though no woman was to be seen. The wind came over the mountains in a great cold sweep, and in the morning he was gone.

The War-Trail of Sin'opa

Sometimes in the camps of the Siksika, when the fires burn low and only the men are there, the Old Ones tell the story of a woman. They tell it with the sound of grief in their old voices even now, and there are none alive who ever saw her. She has been dead so long. It may be that she is only a story, a legend—not a real woman at all—but never say so to the Old Ones. She is real to them. They had the tale from their fathers, who heard it from their fathers and their grandfathers, for it is a thing men tell to their sons and to their sons' sons. Even now.

They call her by different names in different bands, for her story is one that is told wherever Blackfoot men gather. In our band they call her Sin'opa, "The Fox."

She was the daughter of the war chief Oma-kis'kena. They say the old chief was disappointed because his first-born child was not a son, though later he had sons among other children. But she was the oldest, child of his first-chosen wife, and it may be that he loved her a little more for that. So during his lifetime he taught her the hunting skills, the war-craft he would have taught the son he wished she had been. The other men watched her interest in these things with amused indulgence, and, if sometimes they thought her training was not quite what a girl should have, they did not say so to Oma-kis'kena. Her mother and the other wives kept the lodge and cared for the family, teaching the women's lore to younger daughters and performing with patient drudgery their endless tasks.

Then, when Sin'opa was sixteen years old, a bad sickness ran through the camps of the Siksika, and when it abated, Oma-kis'kena and his wives were among those dead.

Relatives offered homes to the younger children. A husband, they said, would be found for Sin'opa, for she was old enough to marry. But she had other plans. She refused the offers of homes for the children. The offers of marriage she declined often with such insults as to ensure that they would never be repeated.

"I will have my own lodge!" she said. "I can hunt, and better than most men. My sisters and my old grandmother will do the women's work. We will look after ourselves!"

And so they did. The rest of the tribe looked on, admiring the independence of the family, and finding unobtrusive ways to help and to protect.

She was a good hunter. Their lodge was well kept. Things went well. But day by day her resentment of her sex grew and deepened in bitterness. Many things added to it—the restrictions placed on girls of marriageable age, the women's rites she was compelled to take part in, the far more interesting ceremonies she was excluded from, the placid acceptance of their inferior status by the other women, and, most of all, the overtures from the men of the tribe—for they say she was little, and lovely, and there was no man who did not want her.

She envied the war-parties above all other things. As she watched the young men making their sacrifices in the Sun Dance, she thought how gladly, how bravely, she would make the vow, and submit to the torture. When the coups—the brave deeds—were counted around the fires, no ear listened more readily, there was no voice quicker in praise than hers.

At last a day came when she could no longer remain passive. When the fires burned low that night and the women and the children had gone to the tepees, the men talked of war and raids, and they planned a raid. In the dark shadows, unseen and unsuspected, they had a listener, who heard, and smiled, and went to prepare for a journey.

All the next day, the camp buzzed as the war-party prepared for their raid. Women stitched extra moccasins, packed bags of food. Arrowheads were chipped and fitted, bows were tested. The medicine man, Mo'ki-ya, burned sweet-grass on a little fire, and made his search for signs and portents. The signs were good, he told them, and Sin'opa, listening, took his words for a sign to herself.

In the dark before moonrise they left, and with them, walking in silence, concealed by the night, went Sin'opa. When the moon rose, she dropped behind, so they would not notice her. An hour before dawn the warriors slept, and when they awakened, Sin'opa was with them.

They brought her to the chief. Surrounded by the older warriors, men who had ridden with her father, he stood eyeing her coldly. She held her head erect, and met his angry look squarely. A little admiration for her crept into his unwilling mind. But no Blackfoot maiden had ever so conducted herself, and had it not been for the memory of her father, she would have been dealt with harshly indeed.

Threats and persuasions alike were unavailing. She would not go back to the camp. "My father taught me to be a warrior," she said. "I will come with you, or I will come alone."

Support for her came from the medicine man. "I read the signs for this raid," he said, "and the signs were good. Send her away, and you may send our luck with her."

"When has *our* luck come with a woman?" scoffed the chief. But he listened, and consented. The warriors went on their way.

Through quiet valleys, over darkening hills, the warriors walked. Then, far ahead, they saw the camp-fires, and they smiled grimly. As softly as night itself, they were moving now. A twig snapped, and they held their breath. An owl hooted, a small animal rattled through the underbrush, and their hearts beat faster. If they were discovered they would die, and their dying would be neither quick nor easy.

Shadows under a cloudy moon they stood, just outside the camp. In barely breathed whispers the chief deployed his men. "Let me go first," said the girl. The chief shook his head, but a sign from the medicine man changed his mind, and she disappeared.

The warriors waited, expecting every minute to hear the outcry which meant discovery. Then, out of the darkness, she reappeared, leading two fine horses. She tethered them, and went back for more, the men with her. Six horses she took from the enemy camp, and when a sentry stirred she killed him, quickly and quietly, and came with his scalp to the meeting place.

When the party returned to the Blackfoot camp, she came in triumph. Standing by the council-fire, the chief spoke to his men. "The daughter of Oma-kis'kena has proved that she is a warrior." His voice rang over the camp, and the tribesmen hurried to the spot. "What reward shall we give this warrior?"

The answer came back, "Give her a man's name!"

It was not what the chief had intended, but he turned to the girl and asked, "Do you want that, a man's name?"

"That, and my coup!" she answered.

The chief turned to his men. "Sin'opa has gone on to the Sand Hills," he said. "Shall we give *his* name to her?"

"Yes," shouted the warriors.

"I want my coup," said Sin'opa.

The chief turned again to his warriors. "Does Sin'opa count coup with *us?*" he shouted.

The answer came back, "Yes!"

The sound of the drums came up like thunder out of the mountains, and the high rolling chant of the coup songs shook the trees by the river.

From that time on, she rode with the warriors, led a man's life. She wore men's clothing while on raids and hunting, but in the camp she dressed as the women dressed. She was little, and very lovely, the Old Ones say, and the men she rode with thought of her often, not always as the warrior she was. And the women hated her.

As she grew older, she counted many a coup of horses and other trophies, many a scalp. In the camp she was silent and withdrawn, knowing well the hostility of the women. But on the trail with the warriors she was happy, and by the fires there was laughter and camaraderie, though no man dared touch her. In battle she was savage; to the weak or the cowardly she was cruel, but for a wounded or a dying warrior her hands were gentle and her voice was kind. The men she rode with came to believe that where she led, they could not be defeated.

When she was past her twentieth year they made her a

war chief. In the lodges of the Ku'tenai, the At'sina, and the Pek-sik-siné-ta-pe, men shivered when her name was mentioned.

Then a night came, a raid on the Ku'tenai. The alarm was given. Someone tripped? A horse neighed? It doesn't matter now. The warriors of the Ku'tenai poured out of their lodges, and our men fled. When they gathered again, Sin'opa was not with them.

The Siksika went back into that camp like a hailstorm. They killed every Ku'tenai, warrior or not, who stood in their path. The poles from the lodges fed the fires, and by that light they searched for and found their chief, dying. They lifted her gently, and brought her out and she was dead before morning.

They brought her body home, all the long way to the Blackfoot camps, the scalps they had taken from the Ku'tenai tied to her dead hands. She sat by the council-fire, dead, and they counted her coup for her, counted the scalps she held in her hands as part of it. They counted all her coups, one last time.

Then they put her body in her own tepee, with all her trophies, her weapons, her men's clothing. The tribe moved away, and they left her there.

But after a while, her own warriors, the men she had ridden with, came back. In the lodge beside her body they put women's clothing, the tools women use, the trinkets women love, even a tiny moss-bag for a baby, for the thought had come to them that maybe, in the Sand Hills, she would be content to be a woman, and it might be that she would want these things.

She is a legend now. Maybe she is *only* a legend, one of that company of women who, because they were never truly possessed by any man, can be something to all men.

Maybe that is why our men, with the cadence of old sorrow in their voices, still tell this story to their sons.

*A-ne'ma-ye ek'ko tsis**

---

*The kettle has boiled dry.

Calf Looking's Wife

This is the story of the Blackfoot chief O-ne-sta-me, or Calf Looking, and his faithless wife Po-no-k-a-ke-wa, or Elk Woman.

It was early spring, and our people were camped south of the Little Bow, when the camp was attacked by a war-party of Crow Indians. With some difficulty, they were driven off, and the Blackfoot were left jubilantly victorious. When the dust of battle had cleared, however, and the losses were counted, it was discovered that the wife of Calf Looking was missing, undoubtedly taken prisoner.

She was a pretty girl, this Elk Woman. Her husband, who loved her dearly, did all he could to please her, so that the other women called her spoiled and lazy, and many of the men shook their heads, agreeing that no good came of indulging women. There were even some who whispered that maybe the Crows had a willing captive, for surely, in the rout of their forces, a young and agile woman could have escaped.

However that might be, Elk Woman was gone, her husband was inconsolable, and her two children needed their mother's care badly.

One morning, Calf Looking took his best horse, dressed himself in his best clothes, and rode around the camp, waving a robe over his head and singing war songs. This was the manner of notifying the rest of the tribe that one wished to form a war-party. When he had circled all the tepees, he returned to his own lodge to await the arrival of the warriors he had summoned.

The people, even the ones who thought he was well rid of his wife, had a good deal of sympathy for him, and a large number of men soon gathered at the tepee. Calf Looking lit his pipe and passed it around the tepee. All who smoked were indicating their willingness to accompany him on the search for his wife. When the pipe had made the rounds, Calf Looking said to the men in the lodge, "Here are my brothers and the brothers of my wife. Since we are the most concerned, we shall go first. If we are unable to rescue her, or if anything happens to us, the rest of you may go."

So Calf Looking and six young men left. They had travelled some days when they came upon a camp of Crows who were just finishing their Sun Dance. The seven men concealed themselves on a hillside overlooking the tepees.

As soon as it was dark, Calf Looking made his way down the hill to a spring where he had seen women getting water. There he concealed himself in a tiny cave. Shortly after daybreak, his wife came to the spring, alone.

Calf Looking crept from his hiding-place and caught her in his arms. "I came for you, and I have found you," he said exultantly. "My brothers and yours are waiting up there on the hill to take you home to our children. Hurry, we must get away as soon as possible!"

"Oh," said Elk Woman, "I am so glad you have come, but can you not wait till I get some clothes from my tepee? The chief, who is my husband here, is going out hunting and I can easily slip away and join you."

Calf Looking told her exactly where the other men were hidden, and bade her join them as soon as possible, since every minute they lingered increased the chances of detection. Then he went back to his companions and Elk Woman returned to the Crow camp.

As Elk Woman drew near the tepee, she bent down quickly, picked up some old black ashes and put them in her mouth. Then she threw herself on the ground, moaning and twitching. People came running, the medicine man was summoned, and, after she had been treated with various remedies, she pretended to be restored to consciousness. "It was the Sun that affected me," she declared. "While my spirit was away, he told me that over there" (pointing to the hill where the men were hidden) "there are seven men. The Sun wants you to go there and kill all but the leader. He has very powerful medicine. You are to take him prisoner, and bring him to my tepee."

Upon hearing this, the Crows seized their weapons and streamed out toward the hill. The Blackfoot, who realized that they had been betrayed, met them at the bottom of the hill. The six young men were killed, and Calf Looking, a prisoner, was brought into the tepee of his faithless wife.

The Crow chief, admiring a brave man, ordered the women to bring food to his prisoner. Calf Looking ate and drank. Then he said bitterly to his wife who was watching him with a smile on her face, "You are just as worthless as the old women said! Look what you have done!"

The Crow chief said to the woman, "What does he say?"

Elk Woman smirked. "He says that you should put the ashes from that pipe you are smoking on his chest."

"Very well," said the chief. Two Crow warriors threw Calf Looking down onto the ground and held him while the chief emptied the burning embers from his pipe onto the naked chest of his captive.

Calf Looking struggled back to his feet. "I am sorry I came looking for you. I wouldn't take you back now for anything!" he shouted at Elk Woman.

"What does he say?" said the Crow chief.

"He says," said Elk Woman, giving her husband a venomous look, " 'Boil some water, and pour it over my head!' "

"What he says, do," said the Crow chief.

Now, there was in the tepee an old woman who knew some Blackfoot. She was quite certain from the words she understood that Elk Woman was falsely translating. And she thoroughly detested Elk Woman, whose arrogance had not endeared her to the Crow any more than it had to the Blackfoot. She reasoned thus: "That Blackfoot would never tell our men to do these things to him. He is some relation to that woman, perhaps her husband, and a chief. I will stay here, and if they do not kill him outright, I will try to save him."

When the water was boiling, Calf Looking was pushed flat on his face and the scalding water was poured over his head while the sadistic Elk Woman laughed gleefully.

"What are you telling them, that they do this to me?" cried Calf Looking. "I wish I had beaten you!"

"Well," said the Crow chief, who knew perfectly well that Elk Woman was lying, "what does he want this time?"

"Now he says, 'Cross two poles, tie me to them, and offer me as a sacrifice to the sun.' "

"Do as he said," ordered the chief. "He is a brave man. He'll make a fine offering for the end of our Sun Dance."

The crossed poles were soon ready and Calf Looking was tied to them with buckskin thongs. Then with the rest of the sun sacrifice he was put out on a little hill and left to die of thirst and hunger.

At once the Crow chief gave orders to move to another camp-site some distance away.

"Good!" said the old woman to herself. "Now I can rescue that Blackfoot. He must be a chief, and maybe we will rid ourselves of that Elk Woman. I would like to see her get some bad treatment!"

So the old woman told her dog, a very intelligent animal which hauled her belongings: "You get in those bushes and stay there. Don't come out even when I call you and pretend to be very angry. Don't come out until I come and fetch you." The little dog ran away into the bushes and the old woman began getting her belongings ready to move.

"Now, where is that dog of mine?" she said loudly. "I am all ready to go and no dog. Always when I need him . . . gone! E-me-ta! E-me-ta! When I find you I will give you a good beating!" And so she went on. At last she was the only one not ready to go. The chief sent a man to ask why she was not in line with the rest.

"Oh," wailed the old woman. "My dog is gone! My only dog! All my things are ready, but my dog is gone! Never has he gone away like this before. I don't know what has happened to him. Such an awful thing, to lose my dog!"

"Well," said the chief, "someone will lend you a dog."

The old woman cried louder than ever. "Oh, aie, no! He might come back and I would be gone. That dog, he's just like a child to me. You must wait a while. I can't go without him."

"Bothersome old woman," said the chief. "You know where we are going. You can follow us." The cavalcade moved off.

As soon as the others were out of sight, the old woman became very busy. She freed Calf Looking from the poles, dressed his wounds, and set food before him. While she worked, Calf Looking told her his story. When he had finished, he sat silent for a while, looking out over the prairie. Then he said to the old woman, using the dialect she knew, "I am going home now. But I will come back. When I come, I will bring with me a warrior for every blade of grass you see out there. I will have a revenge on that wife of mine that old men will make songs about years after I am dead! You have been good to me, Neksista, my mother, and I will reward you for it. Hurry now, and join your people."

Angry drums beat late into the night when Calf Looking came back to his own people. The Siksika reacted with black fury to his tale of the woman whose treachery against her own tribe, and worse, against her own family, had resulted in the death of six of their finest young men, and the insulting torture of one of their bravest chiefs. The old parents of Elk Woman were heartbroken at the loss of their sons, and the knowledge that their own daughter was responsible. So it was that when Calf Looking a few weeks later recruited his war-party, every man in the tribe who could hold a weapon and ride a horse smoked the pipe and took his place in the line. At the head of the column, next to Calf Looking himself, rode the father and mother of Elk Woman.

Scouts located the camp of the Crows. Moving quietly, with all precaution against discovery, the Siksika surrounded it. Horses were concealed in a deep ravine which ran toward a hill overlooking the camp, and in minutes the hill swarmed with warriors.

At nightfall Calf Looking crept down the hill and into the Crow camp. Stealing up to a small tepee, he looked through the space at the top of the door. The old woman and her dog were drowsing near the fire. The dog, sensing the presence of the stranger, growled. "Keep still," said the old woman. "I have never seen such a dog. Always seeing things, hearing things, nothing there!"

"Oh, yes, there is, Neksista!" said Calf Looking, coming into the lodge. "You should be more polite to your dog. He has good sense. I am here, and the hill out there is alive with my men. Give me some food, and we will talk about tomorrow."

The old woman, cackling with delight, for she had not been at all sure that Calf Looking would return, set meat before her visitor. While he ate she regaled him with tales of the further misdeeds of Elk Woman and her paramour, the Crow chief, and assured him that all her family shared her aversion to this interloper and would help him gladly.

The old woman called in the men of her family, and from them, Calf Looking learned that the tribe was planning to move to a new camp on the morrow. He instructed them to leave their lodges standing and to remain well apart from the others.

Calf Looking returned to the camp of his men, and, after some discussion of the strategy to be employed, the Siksika slept till dawn.

At daybreak, Calf Looking brought out the beautiful black horse which was the pride of his heart. "Which of you wants this horse?" he asked. "I have two people to settle scores with, my wife and the Crow chief. One, the chief, I will kill immediately. The other, my wife, will die more slowly. But there is the danger that while I am dealing with the chief, she may escape. I will give this horse of mine—the best racer in all the camps—to the man who will ride him, capture my wife, and bring her to me. Alive."

A silence hung over the rank of the warriors. No one wanted to face the wrath of Calf Looking should he fail in this task. Then Calf Looking's brother, Ma-ko-ye Es-ta-pe-se-tan (Wolf Leading Along) rode out and said with a shrug, "My brother is feeding me to the enemy! I will ride your horse and capture your wife. I have wanted the one and hated the other for a long time now!"

Scouts crept back to report that activity in the Crow camp had reached a peak, and in a short time the camp would be on the move. When the travellers moved out into a line, Calf Looking gave the signal to attack. The horde of warriors swooped down. So sudden and unexpected was the attack that the Crows scattered in blind panic, women and children hampering the efforts of the warriors to make a stand.

Calf Looking and Wolf Leading Along went straight to their objectives. The Crow chief died from a thrust of Calf Looking's knife. Wolf Leading Along, with a skill learned from many a buffalo hunt, cut Elk Woman's horse out of the melee, seized her reins, and withdrew horse and rider to the safety of the standing tepees.

Elk Woman's eyes widened when she saw who was her captor. "Oh, I am so glad to see you! How are my husband and my children? You have come to take me home? Kiss me!" and she flung herself at Wolf Leading Along, who held her off with one arm, and said, "Your husband is here and your parents too. Wait and greet *them* first!"

This was stunning news for Elk Woman, who had had every reason to believe that her husband had never returned from his previous expedition. Still, she had confident hopes that the glib tongue and charming manner that had so often saved her from deserved punishment in the past would serve her again. Therefore, when she saw her parents approaching she ran to meet them with open arms, ignoring their set faces and cold eyes.

As Elk Woman reached out to embrace her mother, the older woman took from her robe a short stone knife. "This is a gift for a woman who has no loyalty to her own people!" she said, slashing off the end of her daughter's nose, and almost in the same motion plunging the knife into her breast. As Elk Woman recoiled, her father clutched her long black hair in one hand, whipped the blade of his knife around her head, and tore off the scalp of his once beloved child.

The tepee poles of the defeated Crows were piled together. Fire was set to them and fanned into a blaze. Then the dazed and blood-stained Elk Woman was thrown into the heart of the flames and held there with lodge-poles until her struggling ceased.

The horses and other gear taken from the defeated Crows were given to the old woman and her family—a sudden acquisition of prosperity which made bitter enemies for them among the defeated. That is why, the Old Ones say, there are, even to this day, two tribes of Crow Indians. And, even to this day, the old men make songs about the revenge Calf Looking took on his faithless wife.

The Medicine Man's Horses

A'pekis'te ma'pe was a medicine man of the Siksika. My grandfather knew him well. He had great medicine-powers, this A'pekis'te ma'pe, powers beyond a white man's believing. But he was a kindly man, who did not wish to hurt even his enemies. The Siksika knew these things, and the Crees learned them.

This is the way the story was told to me, and this way I tell it to you.

A'pekis'te ma'pe had some horses. They were fine horses, and he prized them highly. Therefore he was very angry when he awakened one morning and found his horses gone. They had not wandered off, for the picket-ropes were cut and there were other signs of raiders, who were soon identified as Crees by the sharp-eyed Blackfoot scouts.

A'pekis'te ma'pe was determined to get his horses back. One day he and a friend, taking gifts with them, went to the camp of the Crees. They were received hospitably and entertained in the lodge of a Cree they knew. They presented the gifts they had brought to the Crees, but when the medicine man asked for the return of his horses, the Crees refused. Some of them laughed.

Then the Cree they were visiting told them, "Our people are going to put up a dance for you. Some of them are bringing their medicine-bundles. It is not good."

The Blackfoot medicine man knew what was going to happen. He said to his friend, "Come, we will go out and walk about." When they had gone quite a way from the camp he said, "We will look for the leg-bone of a buffalo."

When they found the bone, the medicine man rubbed yellow paint over it. Then he said, "Come, now we will look for burrs."

When they found the burrs, he wrapped a quantity of them in a black cloth and put it in the crown of his hat. They went back to the lodge of the Cree whose guests they were, and a crier came to invite them to the lodge where the dance was to be held. The medicine man told his friend, "You sit behind me, so I can shield you."

When they came to the lodge where the dance was to be held, the two visitors were seated across from four Cree medicine men. The Crees had their medicine-bundles spread on the ground in front of them. In the bundles two had little dolls, one had a bearskin, and one had a snakeskin. The medicine men started singing their songs, the songs to bring these things to life.

The first one came alive. The little doll became a little man, and it danced over to A'pekis'te ma'pe, singing a song. When it came close to him, he took the buffalo leg-bone, and tapped the ground in front of him three times. The fourth time he hit it hard, "Hai! Hai! Hai!" and the little man fell over dead.

The next was the medicine man who had the bearskin. He sang a song, and it came to life too. The bear walked toward A'pekis'te ma'pe snarling. Again he tapped the ground three times with the buffalo leg-bone. The fourth time he hit it hard, singing his medicine-song, and the bear fell over dead, and turned back into a bearskin.

The medicine man with the snakeskin began to sing his song. The skin turned into a snake, which crawled across the lodge, hissing savagely. A'pekis'te ma'pe did as he had done before, and the snake died too.

Now there was one more doll, a fierce-looking doll, and they were singing its song. It too came to life, and started walking across the lodge toward the Blackfoot medicine man. While it was walking, the Cree medicine men were worried, and they began to sing "Ai-*hai*! Ai-*hai*!" A'pekis'te ma'pe sang with them, tapping the ground three times and then hitting it. As he hit the ground the fourth time, the fierce-looking little man died too. Then the Crees put their medicine-bundles away. "You have beaten us, A'pekis'te ma'pe," they said.

He answered them, "Wait. Don't go away yet." He took the bundle of burrs from his hat and placed it on the ground in front of him. He tapped the bundle of burrs three times with the buffalo leg-bone. The fourth time he hit it hard, and the burrs disappeared, moving toward the Crees, who all fell over as if they were dead.

The two left the lodge and A'pekis'te ma'pe said to his friend, "Come, we will go home now."

But the other Crees said, "Wait. Don't go home. If you will bring those people in the lodge back to life, we will give you back your horses. If you will bring them back to life, we will give you more horses, and other presents too."

A'pekis'te ma'pe said to his friend, "We will go back to the lodge. We have made a lot of trouble."

When they got back to the lodge, A'pekis'te ma'pe spread the black cloth on the ground in front of him. Then he took the buffalo leg-bone, and tapped it three times. The fourth time he hit it all the burrs came back into the cloth. The people in the lodge were alive again. A'pekis'te ma'pe took his horses home and the Crees never raided a camp where he was again.

This is the way the story was told to me, and in that way I have told it to you.

Brother Bear

This is a true story. I, A-no-wa, maker of arrows, tell you so; for I saw the first part of it happen myself, and the last So-ta-na told us, and So-ta-na is a brave man.

The River of Many Chiefs Meeting was rolling high that spring when we came to the camp-ground. Big Eagle's woman was to lead the Sun Dance that year, and she was not there. Her band had stayed north for the winter at So-yo-po-wa-ko, and so had farther to travel than the rest of us. We settled down to wait for her.

The young men were restless. We had coups to count and challenges to meet, and it was spring. You know, life is very good to a young man in the springtime. Over any hill, adventure may be waiting. There are buffalo to hunt, horses to steal, and always an enemy waiting somewhere, with honour riding on his scalp. It may be that death is waiting, too, but for a brave man the road to the Sand Hills is smooth, and a warm welcome is assured him.

So we waited, and we fidgeted, and after a while we quarrelled a bit. Our elders were happy when someone proposed a war-party, a raid on a camp of Crow Indians which was known to be located a little to the south.

The pipes went round, passed from the left side of White Eagle for the Siksika, Big Plume for the Kai-nai, and Crow Eagle for the Pi-ku-ni. We young men jostled and pushed in our eagerness to be among the first who smoked. The old men looked on, and gave advice, and

nodded their heads in approval; the women busied themselves in preparing the necessities for our journey.

At daybreak we left, travelling on foot. It was nearly
three days before we came in sight of the camps of our
enemies, who were just finishing their Sun Dance.

Aie! They were lazy, these Crows, lazy and confident!
No sentinels! Horses picketed in a meadow, not even
within sight of the tepees! How safe they thought they
were! We laughed quietly; then we stole their horses!

The horses we took we put in a little valley, well away
from the Crow camp. We left two men on guard and
went back to take more.

Then trouble came! Two of our men had been sent to
take horses back to the valley where we were keeping our
trophies. When they were returning to the place where
we were, they saw a lone rider ahead of them, a Crow
Indian.

"We will hide," they said, "and kill him." But then
they fell to squabbling about who was to kill the warrior
and take his scalp, and who would have his horse and
weapons. While they were arguing, the Crow disappeared. Quickly they ran up the nearest hill, and, sure
enough, there was the Crow, galloping toward the tepees
to give the alarm.

Our men came breathlessly to tell us what had happened. There was no time to scold them for their foolish-
ness. (They always were fools anyway—that was why
they had been sent to take the horses in the first place. It
was an errand a child could have done.)

Said Big Plume, "We will meet them at the bottom of
the hill and fight them from there."

White Eagle, who was older, said, "No. Leave just a
few men at the base of the hill. Hide the rest along the
sides, near the top. They will think we are only a small

party and attack us. Then we will run up the hill and lead them into a trap."

The Crows, seeing only a few Blackfoot at the bottom of the hill, left their horses and fell upon our friends fiercely. Our men fought a little, enough to defend themselves; then they turned, as had been planned, and fled toward the top of the hill. The Crows followed, yelling in triumph. Just before they reached us, a few of our men crept down and around to where they had left their horses. They brought them to a grove of trees just below where we were fighting. When the time was right, when the enemy was beginning to gain a little, we turned and ran for the horses.

Oh, how foolish the Crows looked when we fled on their horses! They fired a number of arrows at us, but no one was hit and we escaped easily. We rode to the valley where the other horses were, and collected them too. Then, well pleased with ourselves, we started back to the Sun Camp.

It was dark now, and we made our camp for the night. It was then that we noticed that So-ta-na was not with us. "He must have been killed, or captured," we said, and we felt badly. He had been a good friend, and a brave man. We would miss him.

So, our triumph a little clouded, we went home with our coups of horses and scalps, and we mourned So-ta-na properly; then we forgot him.

This is all of the story that I know about myself. But it is not the whole story. For So-ta-na came back, and the old men make songs about the way of his coming. Listen, now!

During the battle, an arrow had struck So-ta-na just above the knee and made a nasty wound. He couldn't run, or even walk. He crawled into a little clump of bushes and hid himself from the Crows, for he knew quite well that after we had made such fools of them they would certainly have no mercy on one of us. He stayed there till the enemy left and after, since he was at least shaded from the sun. He had a little dried meat in his bag, and water from a tiny spring running out of a bank behind the bushes. But his leg was very bad, and the food did not last long. The weather turned cold and rainy.

Finally, he dragged himself along the bank to see if he could find any sort of food. He found some small birds and ate them. Then he found a cave. By this time his leg was turning blue and hurting a great deal. So, since it was impossible for him to get food, and there was no hope of rescue, he resigned himself to die. "Starving to death in a cave is a fine death for a warrior!" he said to himself.

For some days he lay there. Then one evening he heard a noise at the entrance to the cave. A stone that partially covered the opening was moved aside and a large bear looked in. "Well," thought So-ta-na, "to be killed by a bear is at least a better way to die than by starving." He said to the bear, "Come in, Ky-o-wa."

The bear came in and sat down on the other side of the cave. He looked at So-ta-na for a few minutes; then he came over and pulled off the robe he was covered with. So-ta-na thought, "Oh, now he will eat me."

But the bear licked the wound on his leg, gently and thoroughly, and went out, replacing the rock at the cave door.

So-ta-na went to sleep, and in his dream the bear came to him, saying, "My son, I admire your bravery and I am sorry for you, so I am going to heal your wound and take you home. I will give you my medicine, and you will be able to talk to me and understand what I say to you. I will bring a deer to the cave tomorrow, so there will be food for you."

In the morning the deer was there. Each day the bear came to the cave and licked the wound on his leg. It healed well but the man was still too lame to walk.

At the end of the summer the bear said to So-ta-na, "It is time for you to go home. Winter is coming and you cannot live here then. Tomorrow I will take you to your own people."

In the morning the bear came. "Lie on my back, and hold onto my fur," he said. So-ta-na did so, and the bear carried him safely for many days and many miles, till at last they saw the painted lodges of the Blackfoot across a river.

"Good," said the bear. "I will leave you on the other side of the river. You may find your way home from there."

So-ta-na sat down on the ground and said to the bear, "Come with me, and live in my tepee. You have done so much for me that I do not want to part with you."

"I was sorry for you," said the bear. "That was why I took care of you and why I have brought you home. I am very fond of you, and we will be brothers always, but I can't live with you. We bears have very quick tempers, and sometimes we are wicked. Perhaps I would eat some of your family and make trouble."

"I will build you a lodge of your own," said So-ta-na. "Stay here."

"Oh, go home!" said the bear. "I'm tired of you!"

So they crossed the river, and So-ta-na came home.

Oh, but we were surprised to see him! The chief sent runners all around the camp to tell the people that So-ta-na was back. Then he told us this story, about how the bear became his brother and cared for him and brought him home.

A-ne'ma-ye ek'ko tsis

The Wives of the Wolverine

There was a trapper of eagles who lived on the prairie far away from the camps of his people. His name was the Wolverine, and he had three wives. The Wolverine thought they were bad wives. Whether they were or were not no one knows now. But this is the way it was told to me, and this way I tell it to you.

He was a jealous man, this Wolverine. Many days, when his wives thought he had gone away to hunt, he would creep back to the top of a nearby hill where he would sit on an old buffalo skull and spy on his wives. For this reason there were many days when he caught no eagles at all. At night he came home with anger to his lodge, and blamed his wives, and beat them.

One day he walked beside the river, and a Water-Bear spoke to him.

"Have you children?" the Water-Bear said.

"I have many children," said the Wolverine, "and three bad, silly wives."

The Water-Bear said, "I have been watching you. You have not trapped many eagles. If you will give me one of your children each morning, I will send great numbers of the eagle people to your trap."

"I will give you one of my bad, silly wives too," said the Wolverine.

"No," said the Water-Bear.

So in the morning, when the hunter went out, he took one of his children with him. When he came home at night, the child was gone.

One morning the youngest wife followed him. She saw him throw the child into the water, and she went back to the lodge, weeping and mourning. She told her sister-wives, "That husband of ours, he is feeding our children to a Water-Bear!"

"Do you say so?" said the oldest wife. "I have been thinking that something was eating those children!"

The second wife said, "I think we must kill that husband of ours or soon we shall have no children left."

All the wives said, "We are tired of him. There must be better men whom we could get for husbands!"

So the wives made plans together. They dug a pit on the top of the hill where the Wolverine used to sit to watch them. They covered it with grass and leaves, and carefully hid the earth they had dug out of it. Then they put the buffalo skull that he liked to sit on back in place and they waited.

The next time the man sat there, he fell into the pit, and there was no way for him to get out. The wives heard him shouting with rage and they quickly packed up the camp and moved away from that place. They went back to the camps of their people, and left the Wolverine in the pit to die. When the others in the camp asked them, "Where is your husband?" they said, "He went hunting and he did not come home." One said, "Perhaps a Water-Bear has eaten him." The others laughed quietly and said, "It *might* be true!" They married other men and forgot the Wolverine.

A badger heard the Wolverine's cries for help, and he came and looked over the top of the pit. "Me'sin'skeu, Little Brother," said the Wolverine. "Come pull me out."

Me'sin'skeu said, "I can't pull you out, Brother. The best I can do is to dig a tunnel for you."

The badger began to dig, but in a short time he said to the Wolverine, "This is hard work for us, Brother. Let me call some help." So he came up to the top of the hill and started howling for help. He called all the animals that could dig, and all the animals that could dig came. The bears came, and the wolves, and the gophers, and even the little grey mice. The badger said to them, "Whoever gets him out can have him for a pet." Then he and the Wolverine sat down and watched the rest work.

But the wolves soon tired of digging. They said, "We know a better way." And they all sat down around the top of the pit and hung their long bushy tails over the edge. The Wolverine grasped the tails, and the wolves pulled him up out of the pit.

The badger said, "There he is, now. We've gotten him out."

The wolves said, "Give him to us. Men are always catching us in traps. If we have this one for a pet, he can help us. We want him. Give him to us."

The badger asked the Wolverine, "Do you want to go with them and be brother to wolves?"

"I am brother to wolves," the Wolverine said, and he went away with them. He saw the birds fly south and he ate the new berries. After a long time he came back to the place where our people lived.

The people were trapping buffalo in a piskun, a buffalo pound. Night after night wolves entered the piskun and in the morning the best of the buffalo were gone. So they set traps for the wolves. But night after night the traps were sprung, the bait was taken, and there were no wolves caught. So a young man was set to watch.

He came to the camp and said, "There is a wolf. He howls in good Blackfoot. He says, 'Ne'pu'ko no'po'ka! Ne'pu'ko no'po'ka! Your bait is no good! Your bait is no good!' Do you think we should set traps for a wolf who howls in good Blackfoot?"

In the morning the trap was sprung and the bait was gone. So the next night all the people listened, and they heard the wolf howl, "Ne'pu'ko no'po'ka! Ne'pu'ko no'po'ka!" They said, "There is a man out there," and that night they baited a trap for a man. They hid in bushes nearby and waited. After the moon went down, they saw a band of wolves creeping up to the piskun. The man who ran at the head of the pack led them inside the piskun. He looked at the trap, and he laughed. He said, "It is time for you to go, my little brothers!" All the wolves jumped out of the piskun and ran away. And the people caught the man. They said, "Why, it is our old brother, the Wolverine." And they brought him home to the camp.

The Wolverine took his wives back from the other men who had married them, and they lived happily for a long time. The wives said to each other, "He has forgotten that we tried to kill him."

Then, one day, he tied three pieces of sinew with strands of their hair, and he named one for each of his wives. One by one he put each sinew in the camp-fire. As it shrivelled up and disappeared, so did each wife.

He said, "I am brother to wolves." And he went out on the prairie and never came back.

That is all.

The Man Who Couldn't Be Killed

Down along Old Man's River, in the heart of the Blackfoot country, the wind always blows from the southwest. Sometimes it is a warm and friendly wind—the beloved Chinook of the ranchlands. But sometimes it howls down out of the mountains laden with snow or icy rains, and pounds across the foothills, driving the cattle into shelter in the coulees and the bluffs along the river.

The saddle-string stand hunched and miserable then, heads down and backs to the wind. The Indians crouch close to their fires. Sometimes, when the storm is highest, over the wind and the rain you can hear a sound like the slow, menacing pad-pad-pad and the growl of a giant bear. The Old Ones nod, listening. "It is Es'kyio Sko'ops," they say. "It is the man who couldn't be killed."

If Es'kyio Sko'ops is abroad in the night, it is well that he should know people remember him. So again and again the Old Ones tell the story of this man they call Es'kyio Sko'ops and the white man calls Calf Shirt. For, as is not the case with many Indian legends, the white man also has his tale about the man who couldn't be killed, and it is hardly less remarkable than the one the Indian tells.

In our fathers' time, say the Old Ones, before the Red Coats came to drive the whiskey traders away, Es'kyio Sko'ops was a chief of the Kai-nai, the Bloods. He was one of the Natos'iks, the medicine men whose na'toa'pinau (medicine-power) had come from the Bear.

But he was a bad, violent man who used his power wickedly. His people were afraid of him, and with good reason, for he had killed more than one of them in his rages.

The whiskey traders, too, were afraid of Es'kyio Sko'ops. One day, the story goes, they decided to get rid of him. So they poisoned some whiskey and he drank it. It should have killed him, but it had no effect at all. Then they shot him. But the bullets only made little black marks. The traders jumped on him and tried to tie him up, but the na'toa'pinau was too strong. He shook them off and walked away.

A fusillade from the rifles of the traders followed him as he walked. Outside the fort a deep hole had been dug in the ground for some purpose. Into this pit Es'kyio Sko'ops stumbled. The traders, some of them still shooting at him, threw a lariat around his neck and dragged him up to the top of the hole. He was still alive. He was struck in the head with an axe and still he lived. So the traders dragged him to a hole in the ice on the river and threw him in. They pushed his body under the ice into the current with long poles.

(The white man's version of the story is that Joseph Kipp, the whiskey trader, shot Calf Shirt at point-blank range after the Indian had fired at him. Other occupants of the fort also opened fire on the Indian, and when his body was found in the aforementioned pit, it had *sixteen* bullet holes, any one of which should have been instantaneously fatal.)

As the Old Ones tell it, the next day his people found Calf Shirt's body cast up against a pile of driftwood where there was an open place in the river. He had always told his wives that in the event of his death from any cause they should not bury him, for he would, in four

days' time, come back to life. So his poor wives, who
were the only ones to mourn him in the least, carried his
body to the camp and began to perform medicine-rites
over it. They worked faithfully for four days, but no sign
of life returned to the frozen corpse. At last they were
ready to give up.

A medicine man from the Siksika was in the camp,
along with the chiefs Running Rabbit and Crowfoot and
some other members of the tribe who were visiting their
relatives, the Kai-nai. He offered his services. He stood
over the body and sang his medicine-songs. Then he took
a bottle of whiskey and poured part of it into Calf Shirt's
mouth. *One leg slowly straightened out!*

The medicine man was very pleased. He continued his
songs, but the rest of the Siksika hurriedly left for home,
and the Bloods began to wonder uneasily if they really
wanted Calf Shirt brought back to life. They remembered how afraid of him they had been and they remembered the people he had killed and beaten. They ordered
the medicine man to stop his singing. He protested, saying that he could certainly finish bringing Calf Shirt to
life again, but the men refused to let him.

The wives of Es'kyio Sko'ops wept bitterly. But only
his wives were sorry. They buried Calf Shirt in the trees
and came away, comforted a little, perhaps, by what the
medicine man of the Siksika had told them. He said that
because he had gone so far toward returning Calf Shirt to
life again, he would almost certainly come back, but in
another form. Because his medicine was from the Bear, it
would be as a bear that he would come.

And so, the old ones say, Es'kyio Sko'ops walks the
foothills country to this day, this very day. Sometimes a
grim tale goes the rounds of men found dead in the

93

mountains, marked by the claws and teeth of a giant bear. Often the ranchers complain of the loss of cattle. The Indians shrug. "It is Es'kyio Sko'ops," they say. "No use to hunt that one!"

The Dancing Lodge of Chief Little Mouse

One day Na'pe, the Old Man, was out on the prairie travelling from somewhere to somewhere else when he heard little voices singing. He followed the sound and found that it came from an elk's skull, which was lying on the ground.

He looked inside and found a large nest of mice having a party. They were singing and dancing and having a very good time. Na'pe was envious, so he said, "Little Brothers! Little Brothers! Let me sing too!"

The mice said, "Well, Old Man, we don't mind. Sit there and sing!" But no, Old Man didn't want to do it that way. "I would not make a guest sit outside *my* dancing lodge!" he said.

"Oh, very well," said the mice. "You may put your head in and sing with us that way, but you must not go to sleep. If you go to sleep, you will not be able to take your head out again. You'll be sorry!" said the mice.

"Oh, yes, yes," said Na'pe impatiently, and he put his head into the elk-skull and began to sing with the mice.

The dancing continued till far into the night, with Na'pe keeping time to the singing with his head, shaking it back and forth. He began to get sleepy and he forgot all that the mice had told him about not going to sleep. Na'pe slept.

The mice laughed and laughed. Then they gnawed all his hair off and ran away.

When Na'pe awoke, he found that the little animals had told the truth. He was quite unable to get his head out of the elk-skull. He wandered off over the prairie searching for someone to help him out of the skull. Since his eyes were covered by the skull, he could not see where he was going and he was forced to rely upon asking his way from the rocks and the trees, because all things talk to Old Man.

He said to a rock, "Where do you sit?" The rock said, "I sit on the side of a hill, Na'pe. Walk above me, for below me is the river." Na'pe went along his way. He bumped into a tree. "Where do you sit?" he said to the tree. "Are you near the river?"

"I am very near the river, Na'pe," said the tree. "Walk away from me, lest you should fall into the water."

Late in the day he said to another tree, "Where do you sit? Are you near the river or far away?"

This tree was a liar. It said, "I am far from the river, Na'pe. Walk this way, Old Man."

So Na'pe walked past the tree and fell into the river. The current was strong, and the water deep. Na'pe found himself whirled out into midstream and carried along very rapidly down the river.

A little way downstream there was an Indian camp. The women were down by the river getting water when they saw Na'pe in the elk horns coming down the river. They ran to the camp shouting, "An elk is floating down the river! An elk! An elk!"

The men seized their bows and arrows and ran to the river bank. They were ready to shoot at him when Na'pe cried for help. They knew his voice, and said, "Why, it is our old brother, Na'pe!"

They waded out and brought him in to the shore. Then they took rocks and broke open the elk-skull, freeing Old Man. But no sooner had his head appeared than the women began to scream.

"Oh, look, look," they said, "he has no hair. It is not Old Man. It is a water person! Run! Run!" And they all ran away as fast as they could, leaving Na'pe alone. He went to another camp, but they too thought he was a water person and ran away.

So he had to go and camp by himself for a long time, till his hair grew out again. "Oh, well," said Na'pe, "I sang very well with those mice. I did, indeed."

The Eagles' War-Bonnet

This is a story from a long time ago, when the eagles wore long plumes on their heads and the magpies had short fluffy tails.

One day in the middle of summer the Old Man, Na'pe, was sitting in the shade of a cutbank trying to keep himself cool. It was hot and he wasn't succeeding very well. "Oh, I wish I were up there in the north where it is always cold," said Na'pe.

"If you wait till winter it will be cold," said Coyote, who was lying on the ground beside him trying to think up some amusing sort of trouble-making. "And when it was cold you complained something awful about *that*."

"I did not! I did not! I *did not!*" yelled Na'pe, jumping up and down with rage.

Na'pe's yells attracted the attention of a pair of eagles who were sailing around in the sky. "Why, that's our old brother Na'pe," said the eagles. "What is he screaming about?" So they came down to see.

"Aie, Little Brothers," said Na'pe. "Take me up north, where the Big Ice is."

"Well, Old Man," said the eagles, "we can do that, but you'll be sorry, because if you don't wish to come back when we do, we will leave you there."

"Oh, yes, yes, yes!" said Na'pe impatiently.

"You *will* be sorry, you know," said Coyote, going off laughing.

The eagles came down and Na'pe grasped their legs, one leg in each hand, and away they flew to the north.

They came to where the cold began. "This is far enough, Little Brothers," said Na'pe, "I am cool enough now."

"Oh, no, no," said the eagles. "You wanted to go up where the Big Ice is. So we'll take you right there." They flew on a bit farther.

"This is far enough now, Little Brothers," said Na'pe.

"Oh no, no," said the eagles. "You wanted to go where the Big Ice is. We are taking you there." And they flew on a bit farther.

They came to the Big Ice with Na'pe yelling and screaming, "Let me down! Let me down!"

"Now, Old Man," said the eagles, "you don't want to get down here. You can't stay here. You'll freeze."

"I am Old Man!" said Na'pe. "I am too clever to freeze!"

"We are glad to hear it," said the eagles, "but we do not wish to leave you here all the same."

"Oh, you don't want to leave me here!" said Na'pe. "Very well, then, I *shall* stay here!" As they were passing an iceberg with icicles hanging down from the top of it, Na'pe reached out and seized an icicle in each hand and hung on to them. The eagles flew on without him.

The icicles began to melt in Na'pe's hands. "Come back, come back, Little Brothers," he called. "I will go home with you."

"Oh, no," said the eagles. "We told you if you let go of us we would not wait for you. So now we go home without you."

Oh, how Na'pe yelled. But the more he yelled, the farther away the eagles flew, and Na'pe was left hanging on to the icicles which grew smaller and smaller. The eagles went back to the south country.

Coyote saw the eagles flying south. "What have you

done with my old brother Na'pe?" he called to them.

"Oh, we left him here or there, here or there!" said the eagles, laughing.

"You must go back and get him!" said Coyote.

"Oh, no," said the eagles. "We told him, and he did not listen. Now he can be sorry!"

"I've got a good mind, too, to leave him there," declared Coyote, "but I would miss my old brother Na'pe . . . I think." So he asked the geese to get Na'pe off the iceberg, but the geese had had a quarrel with Na'pe and they refused.

He asked the ducks to go, but the ducks said, "We are travelling another way, Brother Coyote," and they refused.

So he called the magpies. The magpies laughed and said, "It would be funny to see Old Man hanging on to an icicle. We will go just for that!" and away they flew. When they came to the place where Na'pe was, they began to laugh. They laughed so hard they could not pick Na'pe up. And the last bit of the icicle was melting.

As they flew by, Na'pe reached out and grasped a tail in each hand and hung on tight. The ma-mi'as-sik-amis flew away to the south country. But they still kept on laughing and this made Na'pe very angry. "If you don't stop laughing, you fools, I'll pull your tail-feathers out!" he said in a rage. The ma-mi'as-sik-amis laughed harder than ever.

While the magpies were laughing, their tails were stretching and getting thinner, and, after a while, Na'pe's hands slid right off the ends of their tails. That is why, even to this day, the ma-mi'as-sik-ami has a long thin tail.

But there was Old Man lying flat on the ground. The eagles came back and flew over him a few times. At last they decided he was dead, and they came down and walked up and down his body. "Well, well," said the eagles. "Poor Old Man! Our old brother Na'pe is dead!"

"I think we should sing a mourning song for our old brother Na'pe," said one eagle.

"Indeed, yes," said the other eagle. "Certainly we will sing a song of grief for this dear friend of ours! But first I think we should eat him, lest some other hungry person should come along and we should have to invite him to share our meal."

"Yes," said the first eagle. "We will eat him and *then* we will mourn for him."

So the eagles began to eat Na'pe. They each took a large bite out of him.

"Oh," said one eagle, "he is so old and tough that I can hardly chew him!"

"Yes," said the other eagle, "and he tastes simply terrible, too!"

This made Na'pe very angry. He sat up and seized both eagles by the topknot of feathers on their heads.

"Now!" he said. "After this, the war-bonnets will be worn by us Indians!" He pulled all the feathers out of their heads, and the eagle people have been bald ever since. The Indians have worn the war-bonnets.

"Enough is enough!" said Na'pe.

How Old Man Made Snow

Long ago when the world was new, the Old Ones say, it was Na'pe, the Old Man, who made all the animals and the people. He made the men all by himself, but Coyote, who was sometimes his friend and sometimes his enemy, helped to make the women. That's why they turned out differently. At first the men lived by themselves and the women lived by themselves and everyone was happy. Na'pe changed that, and this was the way it happened.

For a long, long time the men and the women each lived in their own camp. As chance would have it, some of them were killed or grew old and died. Na'pe and A-pe'si, the Coyote, kept making new Indians to replace the ones who died. After a while Na'pe tired of this. He said to A-pe'si, "How stupid we have been, Little Brother! We will take this camp of men over to the Women's Buffalo Jump, where the women are living. The men and women can just get married and make their own Indians."

"My old brother Na'pe is very clever," said Coyote, politely, "but how are they going to do that?"

Na'pe told him. Coyote laughed till he choked. Then he said, "My old brother Na'pe is clever indeed! He must be chief, and lead the men. I, A-pe'si, will be your messenger, your camp crier."

So that very day they moved their camp over to the Women's Buffalo Jump, where they found the women hard at work killing buffalo. Na'pe sent Coyote to tell the chief of the women why they were there. She approved, but stipulated that the women must be allowed to choose their own husbands. "And for myself," she said, "I must marry your chief. What sort of man is he?"

A-pe'si assured her that Na'pe was very handsome, very brave, and, above all, very clever.

"Good!" said the Woman Chief. "But the cleverness I will find out for myself, and, if he is so, I will marry him!" She made no change in her dress or appearance but went to the meeting place in the clothing she had worn killing buffalo, thinking that Na'pe would be clever enough to see that she was the chief. A-pe'si laughed and ran away.

When Coyote returned to Na'pe, the Old Man questioned him about the Woman Chief. Was she pretty? "Oh, yes," said A-pe'si. "Very pretty, very good, and very clever!"

"Good!" said Na'pe. "The cleverness I will find out for myself, and, if she is so, I will marry her!" So he dressed in his oldest clothes and made himself look very unattractive. Then he went to meet the women, who were all lined up waiting to choose their husbands.

Soon all the men were chosen except Na'pe, and all the women save the Woman Chief. "Well," said the Woman Chief, "I must take you." But she was cleverer than Na'pe, for he flatly refused to accept her, not seeing through her deliberate unattractiveness. The Woman Chief was furious. She went to her lodge, and dressed in her best clothing and ornaments. Looking very beautiful, she reappeared in front of Na'pe.

"Oh, I will take you!" said Na'pe. But the Woman Chief would not marry Na'pe, and no amount of persuasion would make her change her mind.

Na'pe still wanted a wife. Since there were no women

left, he flirted with the other men's wives. The women liked Na'pe and they didn't mind. But the men were furious. One day they decided to chase Na'pe away from the camp and give him a good beating. Now, sometimes Na'pe was brave and clever and sometimes he was not. This was one of the times he was not.

He ran away, but the men followed him, and Na'pe could not shake them off his trail. No matter where he went, the angry men still pursued him. At last they came to the mountains. Na'pe ran up a high mountain and sat down on top of it to get his breath back. While he was sitting there, a flock of white geese flew over.

"Oh, look at Na'pe!" said the geese. "Doesn't he look silly?" Then the geese sang a long song about Na'pe sitting on the mountain. It was a very rude song, and it made Na'pe very angry. He caught the geese and pulled all their feathers out. Then he blew the feathers down the mountainside toward the men.

There were a lot of feathers, and Na'pe's blowing made the men very cold. They couldn't see Na'pe any more and they were frightened by the feathers, which changed into the first snowflakes when Na'pe blew upon them. So the men turned around and went home.

After a while, Na'pe went home too. He took some clay and some buffalo blood, and with the help of his sometimes-friend and sometimes-enemy A-pe'si, the Coyote, he made himself a woman. At last he had a wife of his own. Just the same, ever since then the first snow comes when the geese fly south.

A-ne'ma-ye ek'ko tsis

The Old Man's Arrows

One day in the Moon-of-Birds-Fly-South, Na'pe, the Old Man, and A-pe'si, the Coyote, his sometimes-friend and sometimes-enemy, were travelling across the prairie. They were a long way from here and a long, long way from there, and it was a cold day.

"Build us a fire, Old Man," said Coyote.

"Where do you see a tree?" said Old Man to Coyote. "What do you burn for fuel on this fire of yours?"

"There are buffalo chips," said Coyote.

"Hah!" said Old Man. "Gathering buffalo chips is woman's work. I am Na'pe, the Old Man, and do you think Old Man does woman's work?"

So not a bit of a fire would he build, and he and Coyote travelled on, becoming colder and colder.

But more and more Old Man thought about a fire, and at last he said to Coyote, "Gather us some buffalo chips, Little Brother, and we will make a fire."

"Hah!" said Coyote. "I am A-pe'si, the Clever One, and do you think A-pe'si does woman's work?"

So the two travelled on, becoming colder and colder. At last Na'pe said, "How stupid we are, Little Brother!"

"My old brother Na'pe may be stupid," said A-pe'si, politely, "but I am Coyote, the Clever One, and I cannot be stupid!"

"We have wood, Little Brother!" said Na'pe. "The shafts of my arrows are wood. My bow is wood."

"And if we burn them up, Old Man," said Coyote, "what will we use for our hunting?"

"Oh, make the fire, make the fire!" said Old Man impatiently. They made a fire with the bow and the shafts of the arrows. The fire burned out in a short time, leaving them warmed, and they went on their way.

Then they became hungry. "Shoot us something to eat, Old Man," said Coyote.

"Where do you see a bow? Where do you see arrows?" demanded Na'pe.

"Aie!" said Coyote. "My old brother Na'pe is weaponless! But Coyote has teeth! Coyote has claws! Coyote has swift-running feet! I am Coyote, the Clever One, and I will go hunting!" Away he ran, leaving Na'pe alone.

"Chase me up some buffalo, Little Brother," called Na'pe after him. Then he went on his journey alone.

He was a long way from here and a long, long way from there, and it was a cold day. After a while he heard the sound of someone chopping wood. So he went where the sound was. He found Nepu'maki', a small bird, chopping the limbs off a huge pine tree which lay on the ground.

"Hah!" said Na'pe. "What will such a little bird do with such a big stick?"

"Maybe I will shoot you," said the Nepu'maki'. "This pine tree is my arrow."

"Oh, is it now?" said Na'pe. "And what will you use for a bow?"

"I will make my bow from these big elk-horns here," said the bird.

Oh, how Na'pe laughed! "You silly little bird," he said. "You cannot possibly either bend your bow or lift your arrow. I have a good mind to pull your tail-feathers out for being so conceited!"

The bird was furious. "I tell you," he said, "I can shoot this arrow of mine as far as I please, and I can make it hit anything I want to hit. You go over to that hill and sit down, and I will show you."

Na'pe went off laughing. He sat down on the next ridge, but the little bird called to him and said, "You are not far enough away yet. Go on to the next hill."

Na'pe went on to the next hill, but the bird ordered him to go farther yet. Na'pe went so far that he forgot what he was doing and wandered off along the hillside. Suddenly he heard a whistling sound. He looked around, and there was the huge pine tree coming after him with the tiny bird riding on it. Na'pe began to run. He ran as fast as he could, dodging from side to side, but still the arrow came right behind him. At last he saw a badger hole. He got down on his hands and knees and began to crawl inside it. The arrow hit him and pushed him right down the hole and out the other side of the hill.

"I must have that arrow!" said Old Man, as he picked himself up. He changed his appearance a bit, so the bird would not know him, and went back to the place where the little bird was pulling the arrow out of the badger hole.

"How I wish I had an arrow like yours!" he said.

"You may have it," said the little bird, "but you must use it only when you are hungry, and use it only four times. Each time that you use it must be a long time after the time before. If you use it more often, you will find that you can neither bend the bow nor lift the arrow."

"Oh, I know, I know!" said Old Man impatiently. He took the bow and arrow and the magical power to use them, and went away without even thanking the little bird.

Coyote came along chasing some buffalo, and Na'pe, forgetting all he had been told, shot his arrow four times. They ate only the best parts, wasting all the rest. He tried to shoot a fifth time, but found that, as the Nepu'maki' had told him, he could neither bend the bow nor lift the arrow.

"Oh, well," said Coyote. "We have plenty of firewood now, anyway."

A-ne'ma-ye ek'ko tsis

The People of the Many Chiefs

In a long-ago time, a man lived with his two wives and his children in one of the camps of the Siksika. He was a mighty hunter and a brave warrior, respected by his people as a helper of the weak and old and a wise councillor to the young and strong. But an accident befell the man so that he could no longer hunt. At first his neighbours sympathized. After a while, when he continued helpless, they resented him, and grudged even the poor remnants of food they left at his lodge.

It came near wintertime when the camp prepared to move to a more sheltered spot. The people packed their gear and left, abandoning the injured hunter and his family to get along as best they could. Men who had once been his friends passed by the lodge of the hunter.

"You are leaving us to die," he said to them quietly.

"Your wives are tender," they said. "Your children are fat. Eat *them*!" They laughed cruelly, and went away.

The winter came, and in a short time their food was gone. Day after day the women found the snares they set for rabbits and birds empty. The children cried with hunger, and the youngest wife said to her husband and sister, "Kill me, and use my body for food. I cannot bear to see the children suffer."

But the oldest wife, The-Woman-Who-Sits-Beside-Him, said, "Wait another day. Three times now I have dreamed of strange people bringing food. If I dream again tonight, something will happen to save us."

The next afternoon, as they sat in the lodge, they

heard someone outside. The youngest wife lifted the door and looked out. A number of young men dressed in wolfskins stood there. An older man, carrying meat, entered.

"We have heard from a long way off that you are to be pitied," he said. "Here is food, but tomorrow you must come with us."

"That isn't possible," said the man. "We have no dogs to carry our lodge-poles, and I cannot walk."

"My young men will carry the lodge-poles and you," said the visitor. "Tomorrow we will go where the buffalo are."

"Who is your chief?" asked the hunter.

"We are the People of the Many Chiefs," said the visitor. "I, Omak'okoyiu (Big Wolf) am a chief; Ksin'a'pesi (Old Coyote) is a chief; Big Skunk is a chief; Ot'a tuyui (Red Fox) is a chief; Sin'opa (Kit Fox) is a chief; Si'nai'ski (Badger) is a chief; even Kai'nais'kina (Mouse) is a chief. We are *all* chiefs!"

"Where are your lodges?" asked the hunter.

"Out there," said the visitor. "The whole of the prairie is our lodge."

The hunter and his family were happy living with the People of the Many Chiefs. Soon the man grew strong and agile again. Only two things were forbidden to him and his family. Never were they to watch while the young men drove buffalo into the pound; and never must the children touch any of the weapons, especially the arrows. So they sat in the lodge with the door laced tightly shut when the young men were driving the buffalo toward the cutbank. But they listened, and heard, over the noise of many running hoofs, the howling of wolves, the barking of coyotes and foxes.

"They are no real people, those!" said The-Woman-

Who-Sits-Beside-Him.

One day toward spring, the youngest child, tired of being shut up in the lodge, wriggled under the cover and went out. Forgetting what he had been told, he picked up an arrow that was lying on the ground. It turned to dirt in his hand. Looking up he saw the herd of buffalo almost at the jump. Driving them were wolves and coyotes, other animals following close. The child called his father.

"Don't punish the child," said Ksin'a'pesi, "but now that you know what we are, you must go back to your own people."

At the camp-ground of their own people, they found their tribesmen starving. It had been a dreadful winter, they said. Huge packs of wolves had driven away every bit of game, and they told pitiful tales of hunger.

"Pity us! Help us!" they begged the man they had left to starve.

But he laughed. " 'Your wives are tender,' you told *me*," he said. " 'Your children are fat. Eat *them*.' "

He went away and left them there, and the sound of their crying hung like smoke in the quiet air.

A-ne'ma-ye ek'ko tsis

The Moon and the Seven Singers

Some of the oldest Blackfoot songs are sung to the bone whistle. The whistles are fashioned from the wing-bones of eagles or hawks, and are often beautifully ornamented. They are seldom seen any more, though some of the tribal elders still possess and cherish them. The Old Ones tell a story about how the whistles first came to our people—the legend of The Moon and the Seven Singers.

It was a long, long time ago, the Old Ones say, when the Sky People were somehow much closer to the Blackfoot than they are now, when the High Gods concerned themselves more with the affairs of men.

For many moons, the buffalo had gone from the prairie and the Indian people were starving. One by one the old people had gone away alone out on the prairie to die, knowing that while they remained in the camp the tiny store of food would be shared with them. Mothers wept for their children, who lay in the ragged lodges, too weak now even to cry. Day by day, hunters went out in frantic search for food. They came back empty-handed, or with only a few tiny birds, or some small, poor animal.

Among the hunters was a young man, a warrior named Moon Eagle. He was younger than the others and they paid little attention to him. When the others had tried all their hunting skills and invoked all their medicine-powers in vain, they said to Moon Eagle, "What is it that pities you?"

He said, "I am pitied by eagles."

The other hunters said, "The eagle sees everywhere. Perhaps he sees buffalo. Do you have pity for the children?"

Moon Eagle said, "I have great pity for the children. I will go."

He went away by himself out on the prairie to sacrifice to the Sky People and to pray for help. He cut off the ends of his fingers, and he called the eagle, his medicine-power, to come for his sacrifice. After some days, weak from thirst, hunger, and the loss of blood, he had a medicine-dream, and the eagle came.

In his dream-vision the eagle ordered him to go to a certain place near the river where he would find a large rock with a hollow place on the top of it. In this depression he would find the skeleton of an eagle. He was to take the wing-bones and build a fire over the rest of the bones. He would let the fire die down, then build it up again four times, and on each fire he was to burn sweet-grass. During this time he was to fashion a bone whistle as the eagle directed.

Moon Eagle hastened to find the rock and to do as he had been directed. When the fire had burned low for the fourth time the whistle was completed. Moon Eagle put it to his lips and blew.

The first time he blew the whistle, the moon disappeared from the sky. Seven times more he blew it, and when the echo of the seventh had died away, he heard a strange, beautiful song. It drifted on the night wind, and to his mind came all the lovely sounds he knew—the wind in the trees, and birds singing, and little rivers running, and the laughter of children. And somewhere in it, a long way off, the weird, wild howl of wolves.

The singing came closer, and he saw, walking slowly toward him over the prairie, a beautiful girl dressed in strange, lovely feathered robes. A sparkle like sunlight on water glinted on her smooth braids and her feet in moccasins were ornamented like the wings of birds. She was followed by seven singers dressed in the same way, each carrying a small, ornamented drum.

"You called us," she said. "What do you want?"

"My people are starving," said Moon Eagle. "Give me food for them."

"Give me the whistle," she said.

She blew the whistle four times, then handed it to the first of the singers. He blew it and gave it to the next in line. Four times the whistle was passed down the line of singers, and as each man blew it for the fourth time he turned into a large wolf.

"Bring me buffalo!" the girl commanded, and the singer-wolves raced away across the prairie.

Soon Moon Eagle heard the sound of many running hoofs.

"Your people will have food now," said the girl, smiling. Then she took the whistle again and blew it four times. The seven wolves came running to her, and as they came the stars in the sky grew very bright. The Wolf Road, that pathway of stars the white man calls the Milky Way, swung around, and one end of it came down to touch the ground where they stood.

"Who are you?" cried Moon Eagle.

"I am the Moon," said the girl. "My singers are the Seven Wolves." Then she turned and, followed by the Seven Singers, went back up the Wolf Road into the Sky Country.

The Moon and the Seven Wolves—the stars of the dipper—shone brightly in the sky again. Moon Eagle summoned his people to the hunt, and the long famine was over. He kept the bone whistle, and, though never

again could anyone call down the Sky People with it, it
was used for many years in the rituals of our tribe.

A-ne'ma-ye ek'ko tsis

The Blue End of the World

This is a story from so long ago that even the oldest of the Old Ones dimly remember it. In that far-away time, in the camp of the Siksika there lived a girl who was most beautiful. Her father was a warrior and respected in the tribe as a mighty hunter and a rich man. Many were the young men who sought to marry her. They came dressed in fine clothes and bearing fine gifts to her father. To each he said, "I will not choose her husband. Go, speak to her."

The young men went happily, each sure that he would be chosen. But the girl laughed at them, and teased them, saying, "My father's lodge is large and comfortable. What have you to give that is better?" Often, too, she said cruel and humiliating things to them, and they came to hate her.

Now, among the young men of the tribe was an orphan, who lived in a shabby lodge with his only relative, his young sister. He too wanted the beautiful daughter of the war chief, but he had never come wooing her. He had no fine clothes to wear or fine gifts to bring. More than that, his face was disfigured by a hideous scar, which he had carried all his life.

The people of the camp were none too kind to these orphans. Often they went cold and hungry. Often the little sister wept bitterly over the cruel taunting of their fellow tribesmen.

Many moons went by and still the war chief's daughter had not chosen a husband. The women of the camp

116

said spitefully, "She waits for a man from a star. None of our men is good enough for her."

After a while, when the girl still refused all who wished to marry her, the poor orphan began to think that there might be a chance for him. He had no father or uncle to speak for him. So he asked his young sister to speak to the girl. She wept, and begged him to forget his desires, because she knew that to approach the war chief's daughter would only bring a taunting refusal, and persecution more cruel than that which they already were enduring. But her brother insisted, and as a well-brought-up Blackfoot maiden, she obeyed him.

She covered her face with her robe and waited for the war chief's daughter by the path where the women carried water from the river. When the beautiful girl came by, the little sister said, "I come to speak for a man who wishes to marry you. Will you listen to me?"

The war chief's daughter felt a little pity for the sister and she said, "Well, I will listen to you. But whom do you speak for?" For she had not even thought about the poor young man. When the little sister told her, she laughed and said, "Tell your brother that no man has pleased me. Tell him that if he will go to the Sun and have that scar taken from his face, I will love him, and marry him." She went away laughing and the little sister wept with humiliation beside the path.

An old medicine woman came along. She was gathering herbs for her medicines in the woods by the river, and she stopped to ask why the little girl wept so bitterly. When she had heard the story she said, "Tell your brother what the girl said. Then tell him to come to my lodge tonight at the rising of the moon." The little sister, comforted a bit, did as she was told.

That night when the moon rose, the young man came

to the lodge of the old woman. She said, "I have pitied you and your little sister. I have it in my mind to do something for you." The young man said eagerly, "Can you take this scar from my face?"

"That is beyond my power," the old medicine woman said, "but if you will be brave enough, I can perhaps send you to those who will help."

"I will go anywhere," said the young man.

"Take these moccasins," the old woman said. "Go down where the world turns blue, and when you come to the blue end of the world your scar will be healed. But you must go a long way for that. Now, take these moccasins, and wear them till you come to the lodge of my sister. Then put them with their heels behind and they'll come home to me. My sister will send you farther on your way."

He took the moccasins. And, down where the world turns blue, he came to a lonely lodge with one old woman. He took the moccasins off his feet and put them with their heels behind, and they went home to the old medicine woman.

The old woman gave him food. Then she asked, "Why do you travel?"

"I travel because of this scar of mine. Can you take it away?"

"No," she said. "There is a way, but I do not know it. All I can do is lend you my moccasins. Wear them till you come down where the world turns blue, then put them with their heels behind and they'll come home to me."

He came down where the world turns blue and there was another lodge with an old woman in it. He took off the moccasins and put them with their heels behind, and they went home to the second old woman.

The third old woman asked, "Why do you travel?"

He said, "I travel because of this scar of mine. Can you take it away?"

"No," she said. "There is a way. I do not know it, but my sister who lives at the blue end of the world will know. All I can do is give you my medicine, which is powerful but not powerful enough, and my moccasins. When you come down where the world turns blue, put them with their heels behind and they'll come home to me." He took the moccasins and went off to the blue end of the world.

When he came there, he found a great body of water and a lodge with an old woman. He took off his moccasins and put them with the heels behind, and the moccasins went home.

"Why do you travel?" the old woman asked.

"I travel because of this scar of mine," he said. "Can you take it away?"

"Yes," said the old woman. "When you come to the blue end of the world we can do many things. Lie down now and rest, for you must journey farther than this. The lodge of my daughter is on the other side of the water. You must go to it."

When the moon rose, the young man saw four swans swimming in the moon-track. They came in to the shore and spread their wings toward him.

"Step onto the water," the old woman said. "The swans will take you to the lodge of the people over there." So the young man stepped onto the water, and the swans picked him up on their wings and swam down the moon-track.

The moon-track led to a beautiful country. He was met by a woman, tall and beautiful, who led him to a fine lodge. He was seated in the place of honour beside her husband at the back of the fire, and the woman placed food before them. When they had eaten, the man asked, "Why have you been sent here?"

The young man replied, "There is a young woman who said, 'When your scar is no more seen, I will marry you.' And there were old women who said, 'Take these moccasins and go.' So I came to the blue end of the world, and farther."

Then the man said, "All our sons but one have been killed by cranes. We live in fear for his safety, and it is forbidden to us to touch the birds. If you kill these cranes, and save our son, we will heal your scar. Here are the weapons." The young man took the weapons and went.

He came to the place where the cranes were. The cranes said, "Here is a young man. Let us kill him." And the young man killed them, and returned to the beautiful lodge with their heads.

The woman and her husband made a feast for him, and the woman built a sweat-lodge. The men entered it, and the woman heated the stones. The man poured water on the stones four times. When the lodge filled with steam, he called to the woman, "Let the light come in!" and she lifted the hides on the west side of the lodge and let the light come in. Four times they did this, and when they had bathed, the scar was gone from the young man's face.

The people in the lodge gave him many gifts. At the rising of the moon the swans came again and took him back to the lodge of the old woman.

He had been to the blue end of the world, and he came back without the scar on his face. The beautiful daughter of the war chief loved him and married him.

But he did not forget that she had laughed and would not marry him when he had been a poor boy with a scar on his face. After a while he killed her.

That is all.

The Red Head

In a long-ago time, a man who had eight sons lived on the prairie. One by one they all fell in love with the same girl. One by one each asked her to marry him. But to each one she said, "No. I will marry the man who kills Mek'oto'kan, and no other."

Now Mek'oto'kan, Red Head, was a dangerous warrior who lived apart from all other people on the prairie. He belonged to no tribe that our people knew, and he had a powerful medicine that protected him when he raided our camps. Many a brave young warrior went up against Red Head, and never came home. Attracted by his handsomeness, and his wealth, and his fine lodge, many a maiden went to be his wife, and was never seen again.

The eight brothers were very much in love with the girl, and the three oldest decided they would kill Mek'oto'kan. His pet magpies saw where they were hiding and went to tell Red Head. And the scalps of the three brothers hung from Mek'oto'kan's lodge-poles.

The next two brothers went to kill Red Head. The mami'as-sik-amis saw them also. "Two more men given to me!" said Red Head, killing them.

The youngest son, whose name was Api'ke'toki (White Prairie Chicken), grieved for his brothers. His medicine-power came from the Wolverine, and he went out on the prairie alone to fast and pray. After many days the Wolverine came to him in a dream and told him what he must do. The youngest son went home very happy.

He made his preparations, and then he and the two remaining brothers went in search of Red Head. When they were still three days' journey from Mek'oto'kan's lodge, the youngest son stopped. "You must stay here," he said. "If in five days I do not come back, go home, and count another coup for Red Head!" Then, with the power given him by the Wolverine, Api'ke'toki changed himself into a pretty young woman, and, dressing himself in the fine clothes he had brought, he set out toward the lodge of Mek'oto'kan.

When he came in sight of the lodge, an old woman was skinning a buffalo there. He went and knelt down beside her, helping her with the work. "Is there no young woman in your lodge, Kipitake?" he asked. "No daughter-in-law to do this heavy work for you?"

The old woman admired the fine clothes. She said, "You work well, my daughter. Where have you come from?"

Api'ke'toki said, "I have come from a great way off, from over the mountains, to marry the Red Head!"

The old woman said, "There is no young woman in my lodge, for my son kills all his wives. But if you wish to marry him I will speak for you." She ordered Api'ke'toki to take water to the lodge and offer a drink to Red Head.

Mek'oto'kan accepted the water and said to the girl, "Where do you come from?"

Api'ke'toki said, "I have come from a great way off, from over the river, to marry the Red Head."

Mek'oto'kan was pleased. But his pet magpies said, "Kill her! She has a man's eyes. She has a man's legs. Kill her!"

Then the old woman, his mother, said, "Listen to me. These pets of yours eat an awful lot. I am an old woman and easily tired. Marry this woman, now, and don't kill her. Give me that for a present!"

The magpies still said, "She has a man's eyes! She has a man's legs!" But the Red Head said, "Oh, be quiet, you fools! Do you think I can't tell she is a woman?"

On the fourth day the old woman went away from the lodge to gather roots, and the magpies, who had been fluttering around the tepee saying "She has a man's eyes! She has a man's legs!", went with her.

Mek'oto'kan lay down with his head in his new wife's lap. While he was sleeping, Api'ke'toki took a sharpened piece of elk-horn from his leggings, and drove it into Red Head's ear, killing him. Then he cut off his head and ran away back to his brothers with it.

Late in the day the old woman and the magpies came home. For four days and four nights the old woman sat outside the lodge, mourning for Red Head. The magpies sat hunched on the lodge-poles, and they moaned, "She had a man's eyes, and she had a man's legs, and now Mek'oto'kan is dead!"

At the close of the fourth day, the old woman said, "I married my son to a stranger, and now he is dead." Then she rose and went far away into a strange country, and the magpies went with her. No one ever saw them again.

Api'ke'toki went back to his brothers and changed himself into a man again. Then they travelled back to the camp of their own people and presented the head of Mek'oto'kan to the girl. And they married her. But they remembered that because of her their brothers were dead. So, when they had all grown tired of her, they said, "Now go marry the Red Head!" And they killed her.

Kennaieyi!

The Dancing People

This is a story to tell on a stormy night while one waits for a wayfarer abroad in the wind and the snow. It is a story to tell in whispers around the bedside of a friend who is ill. It is a story for worried people, a story to think of when one rides a dark trail. It happened a long time ago, the Old Ones say, when this was our land.

In those days, when our people might go wherever they wished, they often camped in the mountains in the summertime. Here it was cool and pleasant. They could hunt, and cut new poles for the lodges. They could gather berries, edible roots, and medicinal plants that did not grow on the plains.

In such a camp there lived a man and his wife. He had been a warrior and a mighty hunter. Many times his skills had benefited his tribesmen. The woman had been a good wife, mother of many children. Many times she had sacrificed to the Above People on behalf of others, and never had she refused any aid to the needy ones.

They were old now, and their people had forgotten their goodness. They were not actually in want, because the hunting skills learned over many a long year still served the old man well, feeble though his body might be.

The old woman gathered roots and berries, and slowly, painfully, did the work of the lodge. But no women came to gossip with the old grandmother, no girl offered her young strength to help in the heavy work. Never did the young men lend a hand to the old hunter, never did a warrior come to sit by the fire, to smoke with him, to share the lore of the war-trails.

The moons of summertime went by, and when the first flights of the wild geese cried overhead, the people prepared to move camp. In the wintertime, the snow lies deep in our mountains and there are snug camping-grounds in the sheltered river valleys of the prairie.

Day by day the old hunter and his wife made ready for winter as best they could. They assembled their gear for the journey out of the mountains to the low country, and waited for the men who had charge of the moving to come to help them.

One morning they awoke to silence. There were no voices, no children playing, no dogs barking. When they looked out, the ground where the lodges had been standing was bare. Their people had gone during the night. Not even a dog was left.

Bitter wind came down out of the north. Little snow-flakes whirled through the pine trees. "Mato'ma aut-sto'yiu," said the man. "It is the beginning of winter!"

"A'isa'mo-ts!" said the woman. "It will be a long time!"

They went to work gathering firewood lest the snow cover it too deeply, knowing, bleakly, that they had been left there to die.

Icy storms blew over the mountain country, and the snow grew deep. Many a night the old couple huddled in their lodge, listening while the Storm People walked howling up and down the mountain side. The supplies put by in the summer dwindled, but still the hunter managed to bring food to the lodge, though it might be only small animals, and birds caught in snares. Each morn-ing, the old woman lit the little fire for the Above Spirits. No matter how scanty their food, they never neglected to feed the Earth People. They spoke without bitterness of the families who had abandoned them, and often there was laughter in their lodge.

The days of winter went by. Then, at the rising of the Moon of Eagles, the hunter died. That night, the woman, knowing that only starvation awaited her, covered the tepee fire and, wrapping herself in a deerskin robe, lay down beside the body of her husband. Death would come soon in the freezing cold.

She went to sleep and dreamed that a number of people came into the lodge. There were tall young men, and slender, graceful women, led by an old man wearing a headdress of antlers. "Get up," they said to her. "Build up your fire. The Dancing People are coming!"

"My husband is dead," she said. "I am old, and lame."

"Your husband was a mighty hunter," they said. "The Dancing People knew him well. But he killed only what he needed, and wasted nothing."

"He spared the children," said a woman's voice.

"He is dead," she said again. "I am old and lame and useless."

"Build up your fire!" the leader said. "The Dancing People have powerful medicine. We know of your virtue too, and we have come to help you. For four nights we will dance here. Keep your fire burning, but do not look at us." The visitors vanished.

The old woman woke and built up the fire. Outside the lodge, she heard the sound of many footsteps on the snow. There were odd-sounding rattles and a chanting that rose and fell with the footsteps. She covered her head with her robe and sat by the fire till the sounds ceased.

The next night the dance began again, and the night

after that. Each time the old woman waited by the fire till those outside had gone away. The third night, after she had gone to sleep, the strangers again entered her lodge.

"You have obeyed me," said the leader. "Now, look well at this headdress I wear and the rattles we carry. Study them, so you can make others like them. Listen carefully to our songs. You will have use for them. When we come tomorrow night, you may look at us, but do not look out till our dance is nearly finished." The Dancing People went away.

When the footsteps approached the tepee on the fourth night, the woman was waiting by the fire. She listened carefully to the songs, and when the dance was near its end she lifted the cover from the lodge-door and looked out. The open space in front of the lodge was filled with deer. Slowly and gracefully they stepped back and forth, their small hoofs clicking, their antlers touching. As she watched, the dance ended. The deer, one by one, bounded off into the forest.

She put more wood on the fire and thought about what she had seen. The door-cover lifted and the Dancing People, spirits of the deer, came in.

"Now," said the leader, "you know who and what we are. We are giving you the medicine of the Holy Deer. It is a healing power which you may use always to cure the sick and the wounded. Take these rattles, and sing our songs."

The woman did so. As she sang, the robe which covered her husband's body stirred. His hands moved, his eyes opened, and he sat up and spoke to her. She felt strength and energy flow through her own body.

"When spring comes," said the leader, "go back to your people, and tell them what you have learned. Tell them that the old ones are not to be thrown away. They are to be honoured and their wisdom used. Tell them also that the brave and the good are never alone. When they need help, there are those who will come."

When the spring came, the hunter and his wife made their way out of the mountains and back to the camp of their relatives.

They founded the Society of the Holy Deer, which still exists. Even now, when our people are sick or hurt, they call upon the Holy Deer, and, because healing and comfort can come in many ways, who is to say that the Dancing People do not hear, and help, even now?

A-ne'ma-ye ek'ko tsis